# Crushing Motherhood

Find peace and happiness in motherhood by improving wellbeing through better health and inner-life management

Fenella Buchanan

Visit the author's website at www.themummingaroundcoach.com



The publisher and the author have made every effort to provide accurate and valuable information in regard to the subject matter covered in this publication. The publisher and the author assume no responsibility for errors, inaccuracies, omissions, or any other inconsistencies herein and hereby disclaim liability to any party for loss, damage, or disruption caused by errors or omissions. The advice and strategies contained herein may not be suitable for your situation and you should consult with a professional when appropriate.

Published by VitaVi Publishing www.vitavipublishing.com

Book cover by 100 Covers

Edited by Alison Barnett

Proofread by Alison Healey

ISBN 978-1-7392645-0-5 (Paperback edition)

ISBN 978-1-7392645-1-2 (Ebook edition)

A CIP record of this book is available from the British Library

First edition 2023

For Ida & Cora with a love that's indefinable.

Thank you for teaching me so much about how I want to show up as your mum.

# Contents

# Introduction

### Crushing it

Oh, hi there! Nice to have you here—taking in this little book I've written. At the risk of stating the obvious, given it's right there on the cover, I'm Fenella. And I'm a very proud mum to two little girls. Ida is 6 going on 16, curious, but cautious, with a keen eye on right, wrong and teeny-tiny details. She is loving, but not with abandon. She has a quirky, sometimes clever-beyond-her-years, sense of humour. Her sister, Cora, two years her junior, bulldozes her way through the world with love and joyful chaos. She is sharp as a tack and stubborn as an ox. If indeed oxen really are as stubborn as the analogy would have us believe. Answering to the moniker of "mum" to these two beautiful souls is an out-and-out privilege, and yes, to any "moms" as opposed to "mums" out there, I am a Brit—currently mumming around in a sleepy little village an hour outside London, in the UK. Not that this fact is relevant to what I have to say about mumming around—it's just an explanation for the use of British, English.

So that's us. As I say, at the time of writing, my gorgeous girls are 4 and 6 and—as most mums feel about their small people—they are my world. My chaotic, joyfully infuriating and exasperatingly beautiful world. And I want to say this: I am *crushing* being a mum. *Crushing it,* I tell you. Or, as we Brits are more likely to say, "smashing it". But please, don't read conceit here. Don't mistake me for someone who thinks they have it all figured out. To put it in perspective, I think all mums are crushing it. You are. All your friends are. Your mum did. With the exception of a very few evil anomalies of nature, all mums are crushing it. Why? Because we are doing our best.

I have recently embarked on a new career coaching mums for a living, and I hear first-hand the amount of time, effort and, most of all, love we mums put into raising our Smalls. Like most of my mum friends, I talk about being a mum more than I talk about anything else. Sidebar: This is something I would like to work on going forwards. Just to make sure I don't stay lost completely in this role forever. But that will come in time, I'm sure. Baby steps. End of sidebar.

Point is, I have not met a mum yet who said, "Yeah, I'm just not going to give it my all today because I don't care and can't be bothered." I've met very few who aren't pretty much constantly thinking of the next mum-related item on the to-do list. I DO meet plenty who tell me they're exhausted and feel like they *can't* give it their all, but of course, at that very moment, they are doing *exactly* that—giving it all they have at that particular point in time. And likely worrying it's not enough. When it is. *Crushing it*, I say again.

**Mumming around**

My own mumming around journey began on a snowy morning in January 2016. I'd just been sewn up after a C-section and was lying in my ride-along hospital bed in the recovery room, unable to feel anything physically from the waist down, but feeling *everything* emotionally from the heart up. Quite suddenly, I was handed a towel cocoon with a little sleeping face peeking out at one end. I was asked what this little face was going to be called. "Ida," I managed to say, "Ida Laurie." And that was the "mument"—deliberate typo there, folks—the exact moment I felt my world turn on its axis. I swear I felt the bed move and the lights flicker—and maybe they did, I couldn't really look away from the sleeping face to check what the rest of the real world was up to.

That was a world I had just left behind where I wasn't a mum. My life "BK"—Before Kids. A world in which I'd endured major surgery to transcend into this new one. Where I was now a mum. A *mum*! Oh, cripes. If you're also a mum, I know you know what I'm talking about. I also know you can't really put into words what happened the day you crossed over, or really, exactly how you feel about it. How it can simultaneously be the hardest, most stressful, most unrelenting thing you've ever done, while also being the most rewarding, life-affirming and beautiful undertaking. Here, I'll have a go at some words:

*Being a mum—eesh—what a life-consuming, identity-shifting, awe-inspiring, sleep-depriving, love-cultivating and ultimately downright bewildering undertaking it's turning out to be!*

Nope, still doesn't encapsulate the concept fully, but you get my drift.

So, there I was with a newborn baby girl, pain, emotion and anti-inflammatories flowing through me to varying degrees, thinking, "What in the world do I do next?!" What I did, of course, was consult the internet. I am a child of my time, after all. Naturally, I was hit with the barrage of conflicting advice the world has for new mums on how to go about the role of motherhood. Here we go . . .

Breastfeed because "breast is best". Or don't—maybe you can't—and that's OK too. Let them sleep with you if you believe in attachment theory and prefer to do it that way. Get them in their own beds as soon as you can because you know that in a world where mums handle so much, tiredness is not an option for you, and some independence will stand them in good stead in the long run. Foster said independence but nurture their need to go at their own pace. Create good sleep habits or let them find their own rhythm. Let them take risks—within reason—no running with scissors! But also protect them from as much as you can for as long as you can. Give them healthy food, no sugar or processed snacks—but don't have them be the only kid at the party *not* enjoying all the treats. Keep screen time to a minimum but allow it for downtime (for them and you). Make sure they get enough exercise; there is no counter to this point. Arrange a lot of after-school clubs, but not too many, though they MUST learn to swim. Get them thinking outside the box, but teach them how to conform for growth into an effective member of society. Break up fights or let them work it out, use reward charts, or don't. Use a naughty step or consequences. Cuddle out the tantrums or pay them no attention. Talk to them about emotions or use distractions to avoid them. Let them dress themselves or coordinate outfits, use conventional medicines or natural remedies, hover at the gates on their first day of nursery or walk away and wish them God's speed. And after all that, if you have any decision-making ability left at all, regroup as fast as you can because any day now, you'll be onto the next phase. All the needs will change, and a fresh set of pros and cons will need your exhausted attention as you navigate yet another one of the many wilds of mum life. Oh, and always, always make them wear sunscreen. (Thank you, Mary Schmich and Baz Luhrmann—like I said, I'm a child of my time—see the final few pages of this book for clarity!) (Schmich, 2019).

Suffice to say, the internet and I figured out some of the basics in those early years. Although, by the internet I largely mean articles written by Sarah Ockwell-Smith. Her take on caring for babies really spoke to me in those early years. Significant because it was the first time I can remember consciously saying to myself, "this *feels* right or that *feels* counterintuitive." Something about my new moniker was slowly waking me up to my gut feelings. Perhaps because the stakes were so high. I still took great comfort in having the confirmation of experts at my fingertips though. Ockwell-Smith's *The Gentle Sleep Book* became my bible for a while. I still point many new mums in her direction as a voice worth listening to in the world of raising children. I wish her book *Beginnings* had been around when I was at the coal face of the baby stages with Ida.

Then, not too long ago (in the grand scheme of how long I'd like to live), I found myself mumming around with my girls on my own, staring into the abyss of a future that looked immeasurably different to the one I'd imagined when they were conceived.

I feel it's important to say that my girls' dad is still financially supportive and very much in our lives. He is a great dad and has all our best interests at heart. There is no blame on either side for where we've ended up. I see us both as products of our upbringings and the cultures we grew up in, and we just couldn't find peace and happiness while under the same roof. And *peace and happiness*—well, that's become my goal, as you will see as we go on . . .

## Mumming around is hard, hard, lemon hard

So, there I was, albeit with some support, raising two tiny humans, for a significant amount of the time, on my own. I was overwhelmed and exhausted, not really knowing which way was up, terrified by the magnitude of it all, but determined to figure it out. I mean, really, what choice did I have? Now, at the risk of descending into a negative grumble too contrary to the goal of writing this book, it has dawned on me that we are living in one of motherhood's toughest eras. That's not to say previous generations of matriarchs didn't have it tough. It isn't hard to fathom how lucky we are to live in a day and age where advancements in almost every walk of life bring with them great advantages to being alive. But we also seem more isolated than we have ever been. The old proverb often attributed to African cultures that "it takes a village to raise a child" has been pushed to the back of collective conscience in Western industrial societies in the last few decades. Instead, the objective seems to be a hyper-independence driven by a survival instinct to keep up with the personal productivity requisite to remain part of the capitalist culture at large. With advancements in technology, it's beginning to feel as though many of us are more connected to a virtual world than a real one, and inquisitive, critical thought seems harder to cultivate when it's now so hard to distinguish truth from noise.

In their beautifully written book *Hold On to YOUR KIDS,* developmental psychologist Dr Gordon Nuefeld and renowned expert in the field of childhood development Dr Gabor Maté lament the erosion of crucially important attachment bonds between children, their mothers and other community caregivers in recent years. They discuss the damaging effects of this on the parent/child relationship and on the psychological development of our Smalls. The cause, they say, is “an unprecedented cultural breakdown”, where “economic forces and cultural trends dominant in the past several decades have dismantled the social context for the natural functioning of both the parenting instincts of adults and the attachment drives of children” (Nuefeld & Maté, 2006).

Reading their book was an “aha!” moment overload for me, particularly when they talked about "the parenting instincts of adults". Friends have commented (I assume always with love) that I have chosen to parent my girls a little differently to the models offered by what could be considered “mainstream” parenting advice. I agree. It was very conscious. Both were breastfed long-term and, for a short while, tandem-fed. I never had a cot; we all just slept together on a floor-level futon in their bedroom. I wore them as babies and toddlers in a sling almost all the time and rarely used a buggy. I was lucky enough to be with them all day, every day until they were 2-and-a-half-years-old, and I have never used the naughty step or reward charts.

So many times, I remember making myself feel I was doing things that way for all the wrong reasons. Was I too emotionally clingy with them? Was I being lazy or avoidant in not going back to work sooner? Was I being too permissive with them as they started to form their personalities? Much of this was my own tendency to give myself a hard time, but there was, and is, a social narrative that tries to persuade women to do their mumming around in a way that’s sometimes contrary to their instincts and to what’s best for their children. I remember a midwife telling me in week two that I shouldn’t sleep with my baby. “Why?” I asked, armed with some of the internet’s scientific evidence that backs up its advantages, providing safe sleeping guidelines are followed, "When it feels so nice and is just so much less exhausting." That midwife would be turning inside out if she knew I still sleep with my almost 5-year-old. My instincts tell me that's what Cora needs. We'll both feel it when she's ready to let me go. Ida informed me very matter-of-factly on the morning of her 4th birthday that I could leave her to sleep alone at night going forwards; and we've never looked back. Cora's time will come.

Another time, I was chatting with friends about nursery school. I mentioned I'd found one I loved that took children from 2-and-a-half-years-old. Ida was then 18-months, and Cora was the size of a plum, with a nice strong heartbeat. One lovely friend suggested I get Ida started at a different nursery asap, so she'd be settled by the time her sister came along. "It's so important to get them socialised early on too," I remember her saying. My gut responded silently, *but I don't think that's true. It's too early, and I don't need the childcare, so why on earth would I?* I listened to my gut more and more as those early years rolled on, holding on fiercely to that attachment time with my Smalls. And now, of course, a few years on, I'm thrilled to hear an eminent doctor and developmental psychologist confirm my instincts were right.

Sidebar again: The point is not that I've found expert evidence that backs up my parenting instincts. Of course, I have. We all look for what we want to hear with this kind of research. Also, doctors Nuefeld and Maté are not the only voices on parenting out there, and while their claims resonate with me and my experience, who is to say they are correct? To any mum who does things differently, it's important to note that nobody here is saying bottle feeding, using a cot or sending Smalls to nursery earlier than 2-and-a-half-years-old is a bad thing. No way. There is so much at play when we're making these decisions as mums, all we can do is make the best decisions possible with the resources and knowledge we have in those moments. End of sidebar. My point is, what doctors Nuefeld and Maté call the "unprecedented cultural breakdown" seems to be an influential force in that process.

I have a good friend who told me she cried every night for a week, wracked with guilt, as she tried to leave her baby to cry itself to sleep in the evenings. "All I wanted to do was go and pick her up and cuddle her to stop her crying," she said. "And some nights I did, and then I was so cross with myself because I'd undone everything I'd already endured." I found this odd at the time. My instinct was to hold and cuddle my babies all the time, no matter what, and although plenty of other things about parenting in the early years drove me to tears, the guilt of leaving them to cry wasn't one of them. If my friend's instinct was telling her to hold her baby, that instinct should be ringing in her ears loud and clear, untainted by outside forces and acted upon with confidence. Economic pressure and culturally accepted yet damaging "norms" should not be parenting our Smalls. In my view, a mother's instincts should. That is the only thing I know for absolute certainty when it comes to mumming around. It is crucially important that every mum does what feels instinctively right for them and their Smalls.

But how do we really know what our instincts are telling us? How do we separate the truth in our guts from the noise around us? Well, I truly believe the majority of mums do just *know*—really deep down underneath all the external pressure of our cultural climate. That is, after getting past the unsolicited advice of family, friends or Dr Google. And if they can fight through the total and utter exhaustion that is keeping all the plates of motherhood spinning, a mother just *knows*.

In her heart-warming, unputdownable book *Untamed,* Glennon Doyle calls this "a knowing." Her book changed my life and is, in my humble opinion, a must-read for all women everywhere. In it, Doyle talks about this "knowing" that she finds when she becomes still, breathes intentionally and sinks her consciousness low, to a place where there's an unimaginable quiet. As she describes learning to go there, she calls it a new level inside her that she didn't know existed. It is a place that is "underneath, low, deep, quiet, still", where there are no voices. What she feels there is a nudge that guides her towards the next right thing. She can pose a question to this knowing, and invariably, it will give her the answer. Now, she is only ever guided by this knowing, which she describes as a feeling of "warm liquid gold filling my veins and solidifying just enough to make me feel steady, certain" (Doyle & Melton, 2020). I remember reading this part of *Untamed* through tears of relief and thinking, "Oh, my word. I'm free. I never have to do anything I don't want to ever again." For a people pleasing, self-doubting, "what will people think?!" junkie, this was profoundly liberating.

So, for the purposes of this book, I'd like to pinch the word "knowing" to identify what a mum just knows deep down is the next right thing for her and her family. My own challenge has always been the ability to sift through the noise, tap into my knowing, pay attention to it and act accordingly. I *always* know when I haven't managed it, though. There's an incongruence between something I vaguely know but can't put my finger on, and the way I'm being in the world at any given moment. It feels emotionally off balance, and I get anxious and irritated. Given that, at the time of writing, my girls are my world, and I am theirs, that is just not a sphere of influence I think will serve them well. When I am anxious and irritated, I don't feel I can provide as nurturing an environment as I want to because I can't hear or don't listen to that little voice inside that *knows* the right thing to do.

So, my goal in motherhood has become this: turn anxious and irritated into peaceful and happy. Find a sense of peace and happiness, where I am operating at optimum physical, mental and emotional wellness, so I can hear the knowing and make the right calls in mumming around. Easy peasy lemon squeezy, right?! No. It's hard hard lemon hard. Life is messy and unpredictable, and I'm not always ready for it. But the universe saw fit to entrust me with two awesome little humans and I take that trust very seriously. It's important that I constantly strive for optimum wellness so I can hear the knowing and act accordingly. That isn't to say I don't believe in checking in with the experts when my knowing evades me. Sarah Ockwell-Smith has been joined by a plethora of knowledgeable humans I follow in the world of mumming around and I try to stay open to new insights, while always trying to feel for the knowing in each decision I make.

It is also vital that I model the care of my own wellbeing to my girls. The hope is, of course, that decisions made by me in this state will positively affect them, but a sideline hope is that I'm teaching them to aim for that same state of wellness for themselves. Then, the greater their own sense of wellbeing, the more easily they will one day be able to hear their own knowings. The instruction to put your own oxygen mask on first on an aircraft has never been a more poignant analogy than where being a mum is concerned. Happy mum, happy kids, right?

## A new way of living

This book contains no advice on the "how to" of being a mum. There are no views on whether helicopter or lawnmower mums are best, or whether attachment parenting trumps a more free-range approach for any particular mum. We are all different, and I do not have all the answers! What I *have* found, however, are a few useful tools and guiding principles by which I can live to foster a greater sense of physical, mental and emotional wellbeing. There are actions I can take daily in my quest to become the best version of myself . . . actions that help me ultimately find peace and happiness in being a mum . . . actions that are helping me *crush it*!

Finding these tools and guiding principles began with what American shame and vulnerability researcher Casandra Brené Brown might call a "face down in the arena moment". There I was, mumming around on my own, spinning plate after plate, anxious and irritated, feeling I was the complete antithesis of crushing it. Looking back, I can see myself bravely soldiering on, doing everything that needed to be done, but forgetting to breathe and getting my butt well and truly kicked by parenting and life in general. I was in survival mode.

One evening, I was barking my way through bath time, becoming more and more irritated by the sound of my own voice repeating things like, "Please give me your toothbrush so I can check your teeth. Have you washed your face and all your hotspots? Let's get your pyjamas on so we can go for a bedtime wee-wee," and "Choose a book for reading time, please." Suddenly, and without warning, I burst into tears. Not just a welling-up, but full-on despairing, breath-catching, messy, uncontrollable tears. The girls were a little stunned. "I'm fine girls, I'm fine," I said hastily, trying to put on a brave, cheery tone as they stopped play fighting and turned to look at me.

I wasn't fine, though. I was done. So tired and overwhelmed, I couldn't speak or carry on trying to get them to bed, so I just sat down cross-legged on the floor and tried to wipe the tears away as they fell. I was mobbed immediately by a small bottom on each knee and little arms around my neck. "It's OK, Mummy, just breathe into your belly three times and then have a cuddle," Cora said, quoting me verbatim. I smiled at her, did as I was told and carried on putting my beautiful girls to bed.

That evening I sat for a long time in the quiet trying to find and listen to my knowing. I felt paralysed with overwhelm . . . like I was well and truly failing at life and, more devastatingly, failing at mumming around. *There's got to be more to life than this,* I thought. *All this "doing" and just feeling so grumpy and unfulfilled all the time . . . there's got to be more joy. And I have to find it because this way of life is just not serving any of us. It's time to make some serious changes.*

I didn't start straight away, of course. That evening I curled up on the sofa with a cup of tea and channel-hopped mindless telly. Even the next morning and the morning after that were pretty slow starts on the "change the way we live" mission. But eventually, my Google searches began to include things like "are all mums unhappy?" and "how not to be such a stress head", and even "there's got to be more to life!!" I began listening to podcasts about what it means to be human and finding happiness; I read books by as many wellbeing experts as I could, searching for anything to help me find that all elusive sense of peace and happiness.

I spent the next few months working through all the negative emotions I was feeling—anger, resentment, sadness, guilt, shame and heartbreak. I found an amazing therapist, and for several months, at the end of each session, she would say, "Good work today," and I'd think, "I guess it was . . . I'm so, so, so very tired." Slowly but surely, as the months went on, I set about constructing a different way of living to anything I'd tried before. It's the way I still live today—mostly anyway (she says with a sheepish wink).

A few months into this different way of life, I was listening to the audiobook edition of *Rising Strong* by Brené Brown, when I was struck by a moment. Not quite as profound as the one where I was handed that towel cocoon of baby, but a moment, nonetheless. I remember it clearly; I was working out alone at the time. The girls were still in bed, and I was huffing and puffing my way through a HIIT workout, with Brené Brown coming at me through my airpods, punctuated by a timer beep telling me to rest or start the next section of HIIT.

Brown had outlined her “rising strong” process—for facing the most painful and challenging experiences, identifying how they’ve truly made us feel, and then finding the bravery to hold ourselves to account, learn from what’s happened and write a new future for ourselves. She was now talking to me about “story”. She maps out her "rising strong" process as the three parts of a story—the reckoning, the rumble and the revolution. The first is the “face down in the arena moment” I mentioned, where we realise we are feeling off-balance. For me, that moment on the sofa after breaking down at bath time was one of them; it was definitely an off-balance moment. The second is about wrestling with the emotions to move from a reactive place to one of learning. For me, that was all those months of learning and “good work” with the therapist. This part of Brown’s book is about owning one's own story. Then, finally, the third part is where we get to take what we’ve learned and integrate it into a new way of living (Brown, 2015). *That’s what I’m doing now*, I thought. W*ow! Our stories are so important.*

I wondered if mine would be of any use to anyone else. Would what I’d learned in the last few months, in the face of a big change in circumstances, be helpful for anyone else searching for a greater sense of peace and happiness in mumming around? In a serendipitous twist, just as Brené Brown was making a salient point about the negative impact of comparing pain and rationing empathy accordingly, a little voice at the back of my head told me I was being ridiculous. What could I possibly have to say that would help anyone? What had given rise to such a lofty idea?

Well, at the risk of exposing a little crazy to the world and confessing just how many voices are in my head at any given moment—and, quite frankly, how annoying they can be at times—I don't mind sharing that another quieter, much gentler voice began to chime in. I stopped my workout and stood still for a moment. I closed my eyes and tried to calm my breathing. *I bet loads of mums would benefit from hearing your way,* this little voice said. *You've learnt loads in the last few months. Why not share it? Your story isn't one of great tragedy, but that doesn't make it any less worthy of being told.* I opened my eyes and smiled into the empty room. "I'm going to write a book," I said out loud to nobody.

In her talk *Call to Courage*, filmed for Netflix in 2019, Brené Brown asserts that vulnerability is the "birthplace" of things like love, connection, joy and wholehearted living. She argues that vulnerability is a measurement of courage, and we can't be brave without being vulnerable (Brown, 2019). So, I am choosing to be vulnerable in writing this book because wholehearted living is exactly what I'm now constantly aiming for. If even just one person reads this book and takes one thing away from it that improves their sense of peace and happiness as a mum by even half a degree, then in turn, I have *crushed it* as a mum just a tiny bit more (see the first three guiding principles for reasons why helping just one other mum helps me).

## Tools and guiding principles for a new way of life

It's safe to say I now have an exhausting (but by no means *exhaustive*) list of well-researched tools and guiding principles I can get behind in my quest to be a more peaceful and happy mum. Trying to implement all of them would need hours a day that I just don't have. As someone with a very active efficiency driver, I have whittled my list down to what seems manageable and incorporated it into my way of life. Here is what I've ended up with . . .

- Identify a purpose in life
- Be of service to others
- Nurture community connections
- Practice gratitude
- Meditate
- Be curious and learn
- Spend time in nature
- Spend less time on a screen
- Minimise the clutter
- Sleep well
- Eat well
- Exercise enough

What struck me immediately about this list when I started putting my thoughts together for this book was that following the first three guiding principles appears to be intrinsic to being a mum. Perhaps that is the reason so many of us find the outwardly unrelenting and oftentimes thankless role of motherhood (particularly in this day and age) to be simultaneously so rewarding and something we wouldn't change for the world. It would seem the very nature of being a mum fulfils the guiding principles of having a purpose, being of service and nurturing those ever-important community connections with friends, family and, of course, our fellow mums. These are three of the most widely championed actions for improving physical, mental and emotional wellness.

Sidebar number three: Before we get into the whys and wherefores of this list of tools and guiding principles, let me first say this: My handiest tool by far is routine. We all know that babies (once they're in one) and small children love the comfort of a routine. I am no different. I do my best adulting and, therefore, my best mumming around when I am in a routine. In this book, I have tried to set out as concisely and simply as possible what I incorporate into that routine and why. In conclusion, I will share exactly what implementing these tools looks like within my day. End of sidebar.

“A mother is not a person to lean on, but a person to make leaning unnecessary.” — Dorothy Canfield Fisher.

Chapter One

# Identify a meaning and purpose in life

## Finding a meaning and purpose

"It's so important to identify your purpose in life. To figure out what gives your life meaning." I come across phrases like this a lot in self-help books, on blogs I follow and in podcasts I listen to about improving the body and mind's wellbeing. For a long time before I had children, all I could think was, *I might just be the only person in life over 20 who hasn't managed to find this elusive and slightly unfathomable life meaning yet!* For me, a sense of meaning and purpose in life equates to something I am passionate about—a reason for doing what I'm doing. Sure, there were lots of things I did that I liked: my hobbies, my career, time spent with my friends and family, but did any of those particularly light a fire under me? Did any spark a feeling of passion that made me want to get up in the morning and live and breathe whatever they were? Not really. Was I, therefore, destined to never truly be happy and at peace? This seemed like quite a bleak outlook.

Cut to a seemingly innocuous moment midway through what I felt was a calm, introspective therapy session not long after the tears at bath time episode. I was talking about my lack of purpose in life, about how I didn't really feel very much "va va voom" about anything at all. And never really had.

"But as I say that," I interrupted myself, "I do have the girls. I mean, they are my world. Best thing I ever did. I can't believe how much I want to love them well and get it right. They are a reason (though, mostly, I have no choice in the matter!) to get up in the morning . . ." I trailed off...

"So, who's to say that isn't your meaning and purpose in life?" came the response.

*Boom!*

In his book *Man's Search for Meaning*—which I have seen consistently and deservedly branded one of the most influential books of our time—Viktor E. Frankl puts forward the notion that man's deepest and innermost desire is to find meaning in life. If that meaning can be found, then anything can be survived. Including motherhood, I guess?! Well, *especially* motherhood, perhaps. Frankl's theory is that there are three avenues through which a person can find meaning in life: work, love and suffering. Fundamentally, motherhood is all of those—hard work, undying love and quite a bit of suffering (with a small "s" in the grand scheme of life, of course). Frankl's theory supports an idea that the mere act of becoming a mother provides women with such a profound sense of meaning, it makes them underlyingly happier in spite of how much sacrifice and struggle may be involved in the undertaking at face value. Frankl said, "Happiness cannot be pursued; it must ensue. One must have a reason to 'be happy.' Once that reason is found, however, one becomes happy automatically" (Frankl, 2004, p.140).

My girls are my reason to be happy. They have brought meaning to my life and given me a sense of purpose. Without a doubt, finding this purpose has brought me more happiness and a greater sense of peace than I did BK. It's fair to say that, in recent years, the positive effect of finding this meaning and purpose started something of a slow-burn spiritual awakening in me. Reading *Man's Search for Meaning* brought me to the realisation that I had to bring what I was doing for a living into greater alignment with what brings meaning to my life. Before my girls came along, I was an EA (Executive Assistant. I had the pleasure of working with some of the most interesting people in theatre, TV, film and music. I travelled in my early twenties, and life until that snowy January morning was not without excitement and "happiness". Nor was it hugely purposeful. I fell into being an EA and was good at it. But I would never have said my life BK fulfilled any burning passions inside me.

The moment I realised that having children had inadvertently provided me with a purpose in life, things started to shift. I needed to carve out a new life where what I was passionate about and the work I went back to after my early years mumming around were more aligned. I immediately found myself engaging with many areas of interest relative to being a mum, for instance, gaining a better understanding of children and the psychology behind certain parenting styles, as well as highlighting the importance of community in raising a child. In addition, I saw a need to ensure I am physically, mentally and emotionally well enough to provide a nurturing environment for them. Breaking generational cycles is very important too, as is helping other mums gain access to their own instincts and find the strength to follow them, no matter what.

During the years I was blessed to be able to stay at home with my girls, I retrained as a life coach, and I am determined to help as many mums as possible through whatever it is they feel a need to move through into a happier, more peaceful and, ultimately, more fulfilled existence. Most of my spare time is devoted to activities that promote physical, mental and emotional wellbeing at home and, of course, to spreading the word one cheeky little *Crushing Motherhood* book at a time.

## The health effect

In researching further, I found that the pursuit of meaning and purpose can also help us live longer and more healthful lives. I fell across a beautiful source of information on this topic, a website called *Tracking Happiness.* It was founded by self-confessed data junkie and happiness tracker, Hugo. In one of his articles highlighting the importance of finding a life purpose, he cites a prominent study in this arena, originally published towards the end of 2015 by Randy Cohen, Chirag Bavishi and Alan Rozanski. This study proved that living a more purposeful life can help people live longer (Hugo, 2022).

During this study, more than 136,000 participants were evaluated and followed for close to seven years. The average age of the participants at the beginning of the study was around 67-years-old. The team assessed each participant by asking them to use a seven-item "Purpose in Life" subscale of the Ryff Psychological Well-being Scale, to help figure out who had a higher sense of purpose in their lives compared to others. The participants rated to what degree they agreed with each item, with a score from 1 to 6. Those with a higher score were deemed to have a higher sense of purpose than other participants.

As they started to face health issues or pass away over the seven years, researchers were able to gather some fascinating data. The analysis told them that among all the participants in the study, there was a lower risk of death for those who felt they had a higher sense of meaning and purpose. After making some adjustments for other factors, the mortality rate in those with a purpose in life was about one-fifth lower than in another comparable group.

So, it seems that finding our purpose in life can not only improve mental and emotional wellbeing, but it can also make us healthier too. But surely, we don't have to wait until we are 67 to see the results of pursuing more meaning and purpose in our lives?!

**How do we find our purpose, then?**

Despite what it may look like—when we are struck down by "comparisonitis" and see everyone we know apparently living their best lives—very few people actually seem to be fulfilling a personal sense of meaning and purpose. A quick Google search informs us that, on average, we spend between 80 and 85 thousand hours working in our lifetime. (Presumably, the only thing we do more is sleep.) Sadly, according to a 2021 Gallup poll entitled *The World's $7.8 Trillion Workplace Problem* only 21% of the world's employees were engaged at work (Pendell, 2022). That's a lot of people spending a lot of time doing something they're not engaged with.

Of course, not everyone is able to do something for a living that brings them meaning and purpose. The marketplace simply isn't set up for it, and often, the need to pay the bills and put food on the table is greater and more urgent. Then, there are those who "don't mind" what they do as long as it affords them the ability to do the things they really love in their spare time. For both these groups, there is the option of "job crafting". According to a *Harvard Business Review* article, which cites research into the concept of job crafting that began in the early 2000s, it can take on different forms, which involve the worker building "the kinds of task, relational, and cognitive landscapes that bring meaning to work" (Dutton & Wrzesniewski, 2020).

In an episode of her brilliant podcast *The Happiness Lab*, Laurie Santos discusses a research project that investigated hospital cleaners who crafted their jobs to bring a greater source of comfort to the patients, while, in essence, they were simply there to clean up after them. One worker who cleaned on a ward where all the patients were in a coma would switch the artwork on the walls around in the hope it would stimulate the patients' healing process. This wasn't something she'd been asked to do but was an example of her aligning her role with her strengths and values to make it more meaningful to her. She *found* meaning and purpose in her work (Santos, 2020).

A quick and dirty thought poll of friends, family, clients and acquaintances leaves me wondering if the problem is about more than just the factors preventing people from doing purposeful jobs or being able to craft their roles in a more purposeful way. Perhaps the problem for many people is also not knowing what actually brings them a sense of meaning and purpose. If a sense of purpose has not yet made itself known, it's definitely worth taking a **look back at past experiences**. Reviewing some of the situations, activities and events that elicit positive emotional memories and writing them down can enable us to see what patterns or common denominators sit between them.

It's likely there will be some trial and error in finding what generates a sense of meaning to one's life. The search might involve some active detective work, and it goes without saying that one strategy will be to **try new things**. This is easier said than done—particularly for the introverts among us—but the benefits will far outweigh the hesitancy in the end. It could be trying out a new class in the area, meeting new people, or perhaps even looking at volunteer opportunities, to see if anything sparks that all elusive *joie de vivre*.

Honestly, the very idea of doing anything like this used to fill me with dread, particularly trying to fit it into the hectic schedule of a busy mum. But then, I did it; I joined a walking group, secured childcare for a few hours one Sunday morning and went off to meet a group of strangers in a car park to head off on a hike through the Buckinghamshire countryside. As I sat in the car across from where the group had congregated, I called a friend and asked her to talk me out of it. "No way!" was her response. "Ten minutes from now, the hard part will be over, and you'll be glad you did it, even if it's crap and you don't have an awesome time, you'll have done it—and got some exercise in the meantime. It's a win-win."

That has stuck with me ever since. In fact, whenever I find myself nervous about something I have to do (whether part of the search for meaning and purpose or not), I just think to myself, *10 minutes from now, the hard part will be over*—and it's more or less always true. The hardest part of anything is just getting over the initial reticence—the vulnerability it takes to be brave. I try and teach that to my girls as well. Even if the thing they don't want to do ends up being something they don't want to ever do again, the part that brings the most apprehension is not knowing what it will be like. But 10 minutes into any activity, and that part is over. It's getting through the fear that's the hard bit . . . and that's often over in a flash, thank goodness!

So, it follows that one of the most strategic tools overall for investigating a sense of meaning and purpose in life is **developing a mindset of growth**. For many years, I didn't have that. Not because I refused to have it, I just didn't even know it was a "thing". Staying on a plateau in terms of personal growth prevents us from seeing challenges we come across as opportunities, it stops us from soldiering on in the face of adversity and makes us closed-minded to new ideas and feedback from others.

In contrast, establishing a mindset of growth and development can see us facing challenges head-on and being open to learning new things. It is this way of being that can open up the world, to identify what brings meaning and purpose to life. What fascinates me about this is that facing up to challenges and learning new things are inevitable by-products of becoming a mum. In recent years, as the challenges of mumming around loomed daily with no choice but to handle them, the learning curve of motherhood felt steeper every day. I have realised how much I have been forced to evolve and be open to new things for the sake of my girls.

Of course, not every mum considers raising their children to be their life's purpose. I have dear friends who find purpose and meaning in their work or their hobbies. But for those who are still unsure as to what really ignites their passion and gives them that sense of meaning and purpose, I'd invite them to look at their "mumming around" life. For humanity, mothering is so integral to the very survival of our species, it's arguably one of the most meaningful things women can do. There might well be aspects of it that can bring us a greater sense of meaning and purpose than we've experienced to date if we are able to really see them. But parts of it tend to be camouflaged by the way Western industrial societies would have us live.

## Finding our purpose in motherhood

As a mum, it can be all too easy to lose ourselves in a million "to-dos". There are tiny humans to take care of, whose needs seem to pull us in a thousand different directions. There is forever a load of laundry and an ever-emptying fridge. There is always cleaning to do, house admin needing attention and, of course, the emotional needs of our Smalls to be met. No matter what the stage of the journey, there is always something to do, and sometimes, that can leave us "meaning and purpose blind". But what if we were to look at things a bit differently? What if we tried some of the following fresh perspectives?

**Enjoy each stage**. So many of us focus on hitting the next milestone, hoping things will get a little easier after that. Another sidebar here: To all those mums with tiny babies, I promise you it does get easier! I say that not because it actually does—it's different for everyone—but because why would a mum with older kids like me promise anything different to their fellow mums in the trenches?! For me personally, it really has become easier. Now, there is more time to regroup and breathe, and I know more about the direction I'm heading in now than I did in the newborn stages. Yes, I know the issues to be faced will be new and different, but for me, nothing can compare to that first step change from person to mother. End of sidebar.

Now, back to how we can enjoy each stage. I have to say, it used to make my blood boil when mums of older kids would say things like, "'Oh, enjoy this stage, it's over so fast!" The implication seemed to be that I'm somehow remiss in not living in absolute bliss with the sleep deprivation and endless exposure to snot, poo, wee, mess, food, emotion and general chaos. There was a time when I could have punched the next person who told me life is about "being in the moment". *Yeah? Well, this moment sucks!* I'd think.

With mixed emotions, I find I'm having to rethink the above paragraph. I'm willing to acknowledge that this stage does go too fast. Blink and you'll miss it kind of fast. And I have conceded to the value of being in the moment—trying to enjoy as much as I can of each stage. It's brought me a greater appreciation of all I'm managing to achieve, which has in turn brought a greater sense of meaning and purpose to my life in general.

**Live with a thankful heart.** When you are doing your millionth load of laundry, breaking up yet another scrap, or trying to prevent one of your children from launching themselves off the kitchen counter onto a flagstone floor, it can be a stretch to feel thankful for what's going on around you. But having gratitude has been directly linked in psychology to feeling a greater sense of meaning and purpose. Learning to default to gratitude can, therefore, be invaluable in achieving the goal of expanding a sense of purpose. Mumming around is a deeply complex undertaking, which makes it chock-full of things to be grateful for when you stop and look at it.

**Kill "comparisonitis".** Social media is the super-spreader of comparisonitis. The photos and videos of friends crafting with their kids or beaming on nature walks, learning the names of wildflowers and breathing in fresh country air, can be emotional wellbeing killers for mums. Meanwhile, in our real world, it's noon, nobody's dressed and the most nutritious thing to pass anyone's lips all day has been a box of raisins. And in a final twist of irony, the kids have spent way more time than you'd like on that very same comparisonitis super-spreader that's just made you feel dreadful—social media. But think about how your own social media output looks to others. Think about the version of yourself and your kids your friends see when YOU are out and about. For a long time, I was predisposed to think that everyone else was doing life much better than I was. But the more I talk to other mums, the more I realise we all think that way at times, and for most of us, it's simply not the case. Mumming around is a messy business, and I don't know anyone who's perfected the playbook. What I do know is that when we stop comparing ourselves to others, we will find it easier to be in the moment, live with gratitude and maybe even detect a greater sense of meaning and purpose in what we are doing.

**Connect with others.** Again, I'm cautious about climbing up onto a soap box and spouting about how modern society has killed the village. You know, the one I mentioned earlier—the one it takes to raise a child? I often wonder if it was deliberate or unintentional, but that's a whole other book, I suppose. What I do know for sure is that mumming around in today's world can be an isolating business if we're not careful. We need our tribes. When I get the chance to talk to other mums, whether it's through my work, on an evening out or in a snatched five minutes at the school gate before I find myself with a small person hanging off each arm, I feel better. The validation and the sense we are not alone that this can bring, alongside the chance to support another mum, connects me to my community . . . another key to unlocking a greater sense of purpose in life.

**Turn your challenges into purpose.** The challenges of motherhood are varied and unpredictable. I remember chatting with a close friend the day before she was due back to work after having her first baby. I asked how she felt about it, and she replied, "Yeah, fine. To be honest, you face so many random things and make so many decisions as a new mum, I'm not sure there's anything work can throw at me now that I can't handle." Well, isn't that the truth?! The reason I mention it here is because it's worth taking stock from time to time of the things you have to overcome as a mum and acknowledging how valuable you have become as a human being. It really is one of the most important roles on the planet. Some mums, as I have with my coaching and in writing this book, take what they start to learn in motherhood and turn it into a purpose that merges into what they do to earn a living. But way before making that jump, simply looking at just how much is achieved in the ordinary day-to-day of motherhood and seeing its value can help in fostering a greater sense of meaning and purpose.

I've heard it said that being a mum is the equivalent of having two-and-a-half full-time jobs. (Admittedly, this is most often said by me as I reassure struggling mums that if their child is fed, clothed, physically well and emotionally OK, they are in fact crushing it!) There is just so much to do! And to remember. And to consider. And to decide. And to research. And to know. With that much-enforced growth of mind in play, how can the process of becoming a mother not help you develop the growth mindset needed to find meaning and purpose in life?

"Having kids — the responsibility of rearing good, kind, ethical, responsible human beings — is the biggest job anyone can embark on." – Maria Shriver

## Chapter Two

# Be of service to others

**Why is being of service to others beneficial?**

OK, so I found my meaning and purpose in life. Boom. Next on my little list of guiding principles designed to bring me more peace, happiness and overall wellbeing in motherhood is being of service to others. Of service? More like enslaved! I feel like ALL of me is in service to others—well, mainly to two small people whose list of needs is varied and long—a task that is, oftentimes, thankless. But OK, I'll indulge all the "well-mind" gurus and do a little research, as that's kind of my thing.

Scientists and psychologists appear to have been studying the benefits of being of service to others—or "prosocial behaviour"—for a few decades now. One such study by Assistant Professor of Psychiatry at Yale School of Medicine, Emily Ansell PhD, found that helping behaviours were "associated with higher levels of daily positive emotion and better overall mental health" (Ansell, 2015).

Ansell and her co-authors took 77 adults through a 14-day study where they were asked to report daily on stressful life events and whether they had engaged in prosocial behaviours such as holding doors open for others or asking if they needed help. The participants were also asked to rate their level of mental health for that day. Not only were prosocial behaviours seen to **positively impact mental health**, but they were also proved to lower the increase in *negative* emotions experienced in response to stress.

Another similar study at Michigan University, authored by Stephanie Brown, a psychologist at the U-M Institute for Social Research (ISR), analysed the data from over 400 couples interviewed over a five-year time frame. The couples were asked about their giving and receiving of help within their circles of friends, family and the wider community. They were also asked about prosocial behaviour within their relationships. In an article about the study on the university's news website, *Michigan News*, Ann Arbor writes that Brown found people who admitted to not helping others were more than twice as likely to die earlier than those who did. She writes: "These findings suggest that it isn't what we get from relationships that makes contact with others so beneficial; it's what we give." (Arbor, 2002). So, aside from having a positive effect on mental wellbeing, prosocial behaviours are also understood to have a **positive impact on physical health**. I have also seen it claimed that being of service to others can help people lower their blood pressure, reduce chronic pain, and as suggested by the outcomes of the above studies, even live longer.

Brown also puts forward the idea that "the benefits of social contact are shaped, in part, by the *evolutionary* advantages of helping others." This idea fascinates me as it relates to motherhood. The idea is that there is an instinctive part of humanity driven by the innate need to procreate and survive which is predisposed to value prosocial behaviour. As a developing species, coming together and cooperating with others would have meant better defence against predators, more consistently available resources and communal care for our young.

So, if there is an evolutionary advantage to prosocial behaviour, it stands to reason that we have evolved to benefit from it both physically and emotionally. While I am no evolutionary scientist, the fact that one of the key factors at play in the success of humanity's survival—decent maternal ability—thrives on prosocial performance feels like a perfectly put-together cycle of interconnected forces to me—an evolutionary ying yang.

Around the time I was contemplating my return to the working world after being at home with my girls in the early years—and trying to think about how I could align meaning and purpose in my life with what I would do to help keep the lights on—I received a message from a friend. It was such a mundane message in the life of a mum, but one that changed the direction my life was heading in.

"Morning, lovely. I need to ask a HUGE favour. Say no if you can't or don't feel comfortable, I'll totally get it, but hubby's away, and I'm really sick. S isn't though, and it'd be great if she could go to school, but I just can't get up. Can you take her?"

Then another:

"Really, don't worry if this is a no, I get it, you might not want to risk getting poorly yourself, just thought I'd ask."

My response was a no-brainer.

"Course I can, love, will pick her up at 8. Want me to bring her home too? No biggie xx."

There followed a flurry of thanks and logistics, but what really struck me was why my good friend, who lived just a few houses down, clearly felt it such an imposition to ask me for this favour? Was there really anyone in my position who'd have said no? Perhaps. In such a time-poor culture, getting poorly these days can feel like the end of the world as we know it. But for me, who, like most mums, is exposed to all but the plague when their little ones come home from school every day, it wasn't an issue at all. It didn't even take a second of thought to decide to help out. What bothered me was that asking me clearly hadn't been so much of a no-brainer for my friend. And it should have been. We should all be in service of each other in this way as much as we can. This little interaction helped me make up my mind about my future—I wanted to do something to give back to other mums. Coupled with my passion for discovering what it means to be a mother, that day was the beginning of a journey which led me to become.

In an article entitled "Prosociality enhances meaning in life" published in *The Journal of Positive Psychology* in 2015, four different studies are cited in which outcomes support the notion that giving behaviours bring meaning to life. I'm lucky enough to have found something that will use and fulfil both. But what if I hadn't? Just like with finding a purpose in life, prosocial behaviour as part of your own life management doesn't have to take over what you do for a living—or indeed, any other part of your life. Prosocial behaviour that promotes our own wellbeing can be something as small as messaging a friend or opening a door for someone. With the constantly giving nature of mumming around already in our back pockets, these small acts of kindness can be enough to give us that extra wellbeing boost.

## Tips for being of service to others

There are, of course, the obvious acts of kindness we can employ daily to be of service to others—letting people out in front of us in traffic, chatting with anyone offering us a service in shops or cafes, even just giving others a smile and hello when we can–may all be seen as an act of service and, therefore, of great benefit to our own physical, mental and emotional wellbeing. Going one step further would be seeking to do volunteer work, joining a group like your Smalls' school parent/teacher association, or involving yourself with a local church or other organisations of like-minded people.

These are all great and extremely valuable places to start. But another, slightly less obvious, tool you can employ to be of greater service to others is **listening**. I came across an alarming statistic recently about the amount of time human beings spend using the language skill of listening in their communication. Compared to the other three language skills—reading, writing and speaking—listening is estimated to be used around 45% of the time, whereas the other three skills are utilised much less. And yet, reading, writing and speaking are the skills more focused on in formal education.

When I started my coaching studies, I came across an entire module on listening and was stunned to realise how poor my own listening skills were. I'd just never been taught how to listen properly. Listening effectively to someone else involves filtering out your own internal dialogue and external distractions, as well as paying attention not only to the words being said, but also to the tone and expression of *how* they're being said. In the coaching world, this is called "empathic listening", and it should result in the listener being able to reflect back and clarify what's been said. In this kind of listening, the focus is entirely on the speaker and can make them feel validated and respected. It can be such a gift to be listened to, making it one of the easiest acts of kindness we can employ in being of service to others.

Another very simple act of kindness that can put us in service of others is to **proactively check in on them**. Even as I write it, it feels like an obvious and trite thing to point out. And yet I have been genuinely stunned on many occasions when I've reached out to a friend I assumed was breezing through life (exactly the way their social media would have me believe), only to find they are struggling, and yes, there was something I could do to help.

Often the thing I can do is listen, of course. Listen, then validate, share a relatable thought or concern and offer my support. What brings a wry smile to my lips every time is discovering that so often, what's been going on for the friend has been happening for me too. We have both been struggling along, forgetting to reach out, feeling perhaps that whatever we are dealing with doesn't deserve the attention of others. I think that can be particularly true in motherhood. I am often reluctant to ask for help from other mums because I know they are just as busy and overwhelmed as I am. Yet, I will help a fellow mum at the drop of a hat if I can. So, these days, I make an effort to check in as much as my brain will allow me to remember to!

Being of service to others can also involve **celebrating their successes**. It doesn't have to be only those times when your friends need a shoulder to cry on when you can be of service. Think about the number of times you celebrate the success of your kids:

"Yay, you just slid down the slide (with me watching) for the 50th time!" (Claps exuberantly.)

"Brilliant, you leapt off the sofa over three strategically placed cushions and landed on the rug, thereby avoiding the lava!" (Pumps fist in the air triumphantly.)

"Amazing, you learned to roll your tongue and raise your eyebrows" (as you watch the entire face of your 4-year-old contort to show you this newly learned skill), "you must feel so proud of yourself."

To a mum, these celebrations with our Smalls come naturally. But I have noticed a tendency in my mum friends to play their own achievements down. And the fact is that every-day mumming around without a full-on nervous breakdown can sometimes feel like a gargantuan achievement in itself. Recently, I've been practising a much more enthusiastic (and genuinely heartfelt) enquiry and celebration with friends whenever they divulge happy news to me. I've been pleasantly surprised by how lovely it feels to really celebrate someone else and have no doubt the benefits to wellbeing are equal on both sides when I do.

**Being a mum IS prosocial**

Being in the service of small people often feels like an exhausting undertaking. But it seems it has its advantages too. Mahatma Ghandi said, "The best way to find yourself is to lose yourself in the service of others." I would argue that finding yourself is, in most part, about finding your sense of physical, mental and emotional wellbeing. Just like the idea that motherhood inadvertently burgeons a mum's sense of meaning and purpose, it seems also to automatically see them using the vital guiding principle of being in service of others. When I look at it that way and see how valuable it is to be in the service of my Smalls, for both their sakes and mine, the job really does start to feel like more of a privilege than a chore.

This has been something of a mindset change for me—I might even go so far as to call it growth! I've noticed I have more patience for what used to irk me in my utterly overwhelmed, sleep-deprived state: I'll wait (fairly) calmly for them to go back into the house for the third time when we're running late to get that one specific "can't live without it today" toy. I will make the effort to change the plate they've been given to a different colour if it seems important to them, because hey, why not? It's within my power to do that for them . . . and it would appear it does me good as well.

I should say here that I do make a distinction between "being in service of" and "being enslaved to"—despite my joke at the top of this chapter. I draw the line at being called into the next room to pass them the water bottle sitting two feet from their arm's reach, which they are perfectly capable of getting themselves. My girls still have family contributions to make and clear boundaries to adhere to. But where I deem it reasonable and within my capabilities, I will always go the extra mile for them and, indeed, for anyone in my life to whom I can be of service. It seems that both my own wellbeing and theirs will thank me for it in the long run!

“The natural state of motherhood is unselfishness. When you become a mother, you are no longer the center of your own universe. You relinquish that position to your children.” — Jessica Lange

## Chapter Three

# Nurture community connections

**Connection—even for the introverts**

It comes as no surprise to me that being part of a community has been shown to be beneficial to our physical, mental and emotional wellbeing. On a basic level, it comes back to the idea that from an evolutionary point of view, being part of a group is altogether more beneficial than going it alone. In a leading international journal focused on the science of psychiatry and clinical psychology, entitled *Psychological Medicine, a study into the effect of social cohesion on mental health* found evidence to support this theory. Specifically, it was discovered that in communities where there is a greater sense of social cohesion, rates of mental wellbeing were reported to be highest, regardless of the affluence of the area (Fone et al., 2014).

I would argue there is nowhere that community matters more than in motherhood. What fascinates me about this subject, however, is how becoming a mother almost throws us into a community that is there for the taking, should we wish to engage. When I think back to my early days mumming around, I remember how many conversations with neighbours were sparked mainly by the fact I resembled a walking eucalyptus tree full of baby koalas.

No matter how individualistic and ego-centric our Western industrial societies may feel at times, there is something about being around mothers and children that brings out a primal, communal desire from others in the community to help and get involved. I've noticed this is particularly the case for older mothers who've been there and got the spit-up-stained t-shirts. Add to that all the places you can't help but converge with other mothers—baby clubs, nurseries or day-care, school gates, soft play, or jungle gym—and the access to finding a sense of support and belonging in motherhood is all but handed to us on a plate.

It surprises those who know me to hear I test positive for introversion on almost every psychometric test I do. Not right at the high end of the spectrum, but enough to make involving with the community around me and nurturing those connections difficult at times. I wouldn't say that "getting out there" is within my comfort zone. But I have come to realise the importance of community over the early years of mumming around—not only for the benefit it brings to my own wellbeing, but also for how it benefits my girls.

The most obvious advantage to being part of a community is perhaps the access to mutual **support.** When it comes to mumming around, however, this comes with a word of caution in our culture. Within it, I feel motherhood can be at its most overwhelming, and so the potential for burnout is high. Yet I hear so much advice about remembering to ask for help when it's needed. This is great advice until the mums you feel comfortable going to for help are just as strung out as you are. Of course, there are times when—as when my friend asked me to take her kid to school—it really isn't a big ask, but I feel reluctant to constantly ask for help from mums I know are flat out themselves. What I *do* feel comfortable doing is sharing my experience and checking in. Support doesn't have to be physical. Sometimes, it can just be the knowledge that you are not alone in feeling frazzled, or a simple reminder that tomorrow is library book day at school. Support can often be shown in the smallest of gestures.

Another benefit to being part of a community is the sense of **empowerment** it brings. That sense of empowerment can be the driving force behind effecting really positive change in a community as a whole. If anyone has ever been in a parent/teacher meeting and witnessed a group of mums working together to improve the lives of their kids at school, they will know just what a force that sense of strength in the community can bring.

I would also argue that it develops the **confidence** of the individual as well. I have certainly grown in confidence since having children. I used to put it down to the immersion therapy of suddenly having to make life-and-death decisions affecting the wellbeing of a tiny human on a daily basis. More recently, I also attribute it to the sense of belonging I now have to the community of motherhood.

The **sharing of ideas** is another great benefit of belonging to a community. Just recently, I went out for an early tea with friends. I was a little behind my friend with my girls, and she was already seated with her boys. Both had iPads and were as quiet as church mice. I was holding a big, pink box file. My friend looked at me with interest and said, "You're about to bust out something wholesome and creative to occupy them, aren't you?" I was—a box of colouring and other little arts and crafts projects. It lives in the boot of my car. Within minutes, all the kids were colouring.

A few weeks later my friend sent me a photo of her own box file with the caption, "Shamelessly stole your idea!" "Awesome!! As well you should!", I replied, with many heart emojis. That is what ideas like that are for, to be shared. This is a small example of the advantages of connecting with other mums, but there are some ideas exchanged within the community that can vastly improve the health and wellbeing of all involved . . . if not actually save lives.

Another mini sidebar: I should also point out that I too had iPads with me that day. I have no shame about having a little screen time at the table while waiting for food to arrive so I can get in some chat with a friend. End of sidebar. Also, the idea of the arts and crafts box file was not mine! Neither is it massively ground-breaking, but it certainly wasn't something I'd have thought to do in those early years if I hadn't seen another friend of mine pull hers from her boot a few years earlier. The sharing of ideas makes both individuals and the communities they are a part of stronger in themselves and as a whole.

Another thing that's developed for me as a result of being part of a community is the **sense of passion** I feel about so many more things than I did before having children. This could, of course, just be a stage of my own personal development, but I can't help feeling it has something to do with suddenly belonging to a community of women I have at least one thing in common with, with whom I can share what interests me. This is something I never quite found for myself when I was younger, and I know that's not the case for everyone. Some people find their communities through what they're passionate about much earlier in life, and being able to share those passions—having an outlet for them—is surely what further strengthens them and in turn, helps to nurture a greater sense of passion and overall wellbeing.

For me personally, it was a passion for wellbeing in motherhood that became my purpose, but recently, with a friend, I watched it happen with crochet! We were having lunch in a park and, in a rare moment of peace when all the kids were running about, she pulled out a shawl she was halfway through making and a pattern she was clearly halfway through writing.

"Oh, now, is this crochet?" I asked. "I've never understood how to do it. It looks so complicated. I can knit—well, sort of—not done it for a long time, but this just never came my way . . ." I trailed off.

There followed an extremely passionate monologue—including demonstrations—about what she was making, why she preferred crochet to knitting, a beginner's intro to the different stitches, what kind of yarn works best when you're starting out and the pattern she was working on . . .

"Sounds like fun," I said when she reached a pause. "Have you thought about teaching it?"

Turns out she had, and there followed another passionate soliloquy about the ins and outs of teaching groups and/or writing a book and creating patterns for others to follow. By the end of this short exchange, I was seriously considering taking up crochet! I never did, of course, it's not my passion. But the point is, her passion was infectious, and talking about it to someone in her community might just have spurred her on to do something more with a hobby she was clearly very excited by.

## Tips for building community connections in motherhood

So, we can see the advantages to taking our place in a community—and just like with finding a purpose and being of service to others, this guiding principle for improving physical, mental and emotional wellbeing is another tool that's made accessible in the very act of becoming a mother. Also, building on the community connections that are all but thrown our way the day we give birth doesn't have to be onerous. We can turn something as simple as the school pickup into a chance to nurture those connections. I have learned to keep a few things in mind when interacting with my communities.

**Be open.** Communities can be found anywhere and everywhere. They don't have to grow up around a specific hobby or interest and don't always need to develop into a formally organised group with a WhatsApp group title and photo! The one or two mums you always tend to stand with at the school gates whilst waiting for your kids can be one of your communities. I hope it doesn't need saying how valuable it is to be open to people you might not ordinarily be drawn towards too. Some of my most fulfilling connections have been with people I caught myself initially assuming I wouldn't have much in common with. We all have those prejudices; they are, sadly, a part of human nature. Keeping them in mind and constantly pushing them aside in favour of connection is key for me.

**Be myself.** A great place to start with finding a community is looking for groups who share the same interests as you. This is hard sometimes. If you aren't someone who always knows what really interests them, some trial and error might be needed to see what floats your boat. In these situations, I always try to keep in mind that I should be myself. I try to move towards what feels right and away from what doesn't. This is about tapping into the concept of knowing which I adopted from Glennon Doyle (Doyle & Melton, 2020). If I let myself listen to my own gut instincts, I can sometimes catch myself trying to fit in where I really don't, and with love and grace, I can move on to look for something new.

**Bring my best self.** Even when I need my community for a grumble and moan, I try to remember to bring my best self to the table. This not only serves me, but it strengthens the group as a whole. Letting go of negative energy will always be beneficial to my own wellbeing, but if the group I am venting to also experiences me trying to move through that negative emotion, it will feel like a safe space for them to be able to do the same if they need to. I try very hard to remember I am there to be of service too!

**Gently keep trying.** I have one community in my village where I'm the butt of a very good-humoured joke, which goes something like this whenever we're introducing a new mum to the group:

"Yep, hope you didn't expect to come and live here and not be part of this gang? Fen won't let anyone keep themselves to themselves!" This isn't strictly true, of course; there was one mum who, for whatever reason, didn't really engage when I first moved into the village and made contact. She has since moved. Perhaps that's why she was more reserved—she knew she would soon be leaving. Or she already had a tight group of friends elsewhere. But I made sure to message her initially, so she knew we were there if she needed us. With the others—some of whom had lived in the same small village for a good few years and didn't really know each other—I set about bringing us together for a few nights out. At first, I drove the project a lot. Everyone was into it, but I was the instigator. Now this little group runs itself. Someone is always popping up with a message about what they're up to with the kids and inviting others to join or getting the ball rolling on a mums'-only get-together.

*"It is not more bigness that should be our goal. We must attempt, rather, to bring people back to the warmth of community, to the worth of individual effort and responsibility, and of individuals working together as a community, to better their lives and their children's future."*—Robert F. Kennedy

As I was researching this quote about community, I came across another that sparked my interest:

*"Educate a boy, and you educate an individual. Educate a girl, and you educate a community."*—Adelaide Hoodless

Little did I know that Adelaide Hoodless was the founder of the international women's organisation the Women's Institute. The good old W.I.! What I also didn't know was the inspiration behind starting its inaugural group. Tragically, Adelaide's infant son died of meningitis at the age of 14 months after a 10-day illness. This unfathomably devastating event spurred her devotion to educating new mothers to prevent this sort of tragedy from happening to other women. The first group's mission was to connect its members socially as a community alongside broadening their knowledge of agriculture and domestic science. This is the perfect illustration of the value of being part of a community.

The discussion around the predilection of boys versus girls in forming communities is an interesting one. It throws up all sorts of questions as to whether those biases exist due to something instinctive in the natures of men and women, or whether we have been conditioned to be that way through the cultural influences we've grown up with over generations. My own experience has been that women are more likely to make efforts to come together and form connections. I think it's a functional instinct—Nature's way of ensuring we will have the support of a tribe of other women should we ever embark on the journey of motherhood.

“When you are a mother, you are never really alone in your thoughts. A mother always has to think twice, once for herself and once for her child.” – Sophia Loren

# Chapter Four

# Practice gratitude

**Be grateful, not grouchful!**

It's no secret that the human brain is hardwired to notice and remember negative experiences. Psychologists call this a "negativity bias" and have put it down to being a by-product of our evolutionary development. As early humans evolved, noticing the surrounding threats could, literally, have meant the difference between life and death, and it's likely that, as a species, we have handed down the genes that are more attuned to noticing negativity. As Kendra Cherry points out in an article on the website *verywellmind.com*, although "we may no longer need to be on constant high alert as our early ancestors needed to be in order to survive, the negativity bias still has a starring role in how our brains operate" (Cherry, 2022).

It's an interesting idea that even though there are no longer sabre-toothed tigers prowling around our homes, our brains are hard-wired to react (and direct our bodies to react) as if there are, no matter how trivial the day's negative experience might be in comparison to being mauled by said sabre-toothed tiger. I have noticed that these negative experiences make a much bigger impression on my stress response when I am not practising my tools and guiding principles effectively. When I am physically, mentally and emotionally run down, forgetting a PE kit or running out of milk can often be the straw that breaks the camel's back. And some days when I'm mumming around, that poor camel is on the floor!

Cue the practice of gratitude...

In positive psychology, gratitude has been strongly linked to a greater sense of happiness and wellbeing. In a Harvard Medical School article published on the *Harvard Health Publishing* website, it states that gratitude "helps people feel more positive emotions, relish good experiences, improve their health, deal with adversity, and build strong relationships" (*Harvard Health Publishing*, 2021). It also cites a study by two psychologists, Dr Robert A Emmons of the University of California, Davis, and Dr Michael E McCullough of the University of Miami, which found that not only did gratitude make their research subjects feel more positive about their lives, but it also resulted in them exercising more and showing signs of better health.

**Gratitude in mumming around**

Gratitude journals are being produced in their millions these days. Writing just a few sentences about things you are thankful for at the end of each day can be as much as is needed to start practising gratitude. I have happily found this technique to be surprisingly easy and effective in changing my outlook. That's not because I have an amazing life, where there is nothing at all to worry about. There's plenty – money, the health and wellbeing of myself and my kids, the international socio-political climate, war, poverty – and wondering where the hell the partners of the odd socks I end up with at the end of every load of laundry have disappeared to?! But what I have found with gratitude as a mother is there is always one thing I can write that I am grateful for that never changes – the fact that I am one. From there, I find more grateful thoughts spring forth . . . even on my hardest days . . . and it makes a difference. Since I started practising gratitude just once in the evening, I have noticed similar thoughts popping into my head during the day too. It makes me gentler in my approach to a screaming four-year-old's rage when I won't let her build a den for her teddy out of kitchen knives!

**Tips for adding more gratitude to your life**

One thing I did in the beginning when I first started practising gratitude, was to think about the **gratitudes of the past, present and future**. I would give myself the prompt of writing down one thing I was grateful for in my past, one thing I was blessed with at that time and one thing I was optimistic about in the future. It wasn't my idea; a therapist I was seeing at the time suggested it, and I found it a really accessible way to start the practice of gratitude. It also encouraged me to rewrite some of the negative biases in my memories and start paving the way for a more positive outlook on the present and the future.

I also have a friend who swears by **counting blessings** as a way of practising gratitude. Once a week—usually on a Monday morning—she sits for 15 minutes and writes in her gratitude journal as many things as she can think of that she is blessed to have in her life. I do this from time to time when I'm struggling and need to remember the good stuff. I am always surprised to find how many blessings I can think of. I usually end up with things as seemingly small as "grateful for the air in my lungs" (although this is, of course, no small thing, seeing as it sustains life). When I do this exercise, I try to be as specific as possible about the reason whatever I am listing is a blessing and how it makes me feel. My mood is always lifted by this practice.

I recently upgraded my gratitude journal to a **WhatsApp Gratitude Swap** group. I was invited to join the group and jumped at the chance. Not only does it help me hold myself accountable to the daily practice, even when it's late and I haven't done it and I just want to collapse into bed, but it also connects me to others and to other people's gratitudes, which I read religiously to further develop my sense of all the good things to be found in life. There is nothing to stop us from starting our own WhatsApp groups if we aren't randomly invited to one suddenly; they are an easy setup and can be such a great way of being of service to others, connecting with the community and practising gratitude all at the same time.

I also practice **gratitude with the Smalls**. After their nightly bath, as we're getting dried and dressed, I ask them to tell me something good that happened in their day, something they are grateful for and what lovely thing they are going to dream about. My hope is that this practice of gratitude just before bed not only serves to benefit their overall sense of wellbeing, as evidenced by the research, but that it might also affect their processing at night to give them positive and restful dreams.

From time to time, I get a message like this from my brother: "You are the best sister in the world, you know that? Thanks for all you do." There's nothing like receiving a **thank you note** like this, and I believe, in general, that people receive and send them far too infrequently. The small act of showing your gratitude to someone else for how they show up in your life both counts towards gratitude practice and nurturing connections with others. A win-win for this wellbeing tool!

### Prayer and meditation

It would be remiss to write a book about cultivating physical, mental and emotional wellbeing without including a piece about prayer and meditation. I will cover meditation in the next chapter, and so I focus on prayer here.

I came to prayer quite late in life. I was brought up agnostic, but with a healthy dose of atheism thrown in. Prayer was absent, excepting any time I found myself in church for an occasion like a wedding or christening. And even then, it was just words. Later in life and since becoming a mum, I have come to believe that my upbringing completely missed the point. Who or what a person prays to is largely irrelevant to anyone except them. The point is, the act of sitting still with the mind—with the knowing—and not only asking for guidance but, indeed, giving thanks, is greatly beneficial to the self.

In terms of asking for guidance, I now understand that when I pray and ask for guidance, what I am also tapping into is the knowing I am so convinced every mum has. It's the knowing that tells me the right thing to do for my Smalls, the knowing that makes me feel icky when I shout at them, the knowing that can sometimes get lost among all the other noise of busy mum-life, but that's always there if I stop and look for it.

In terms of giving thanks, I remember when I was just starting to understand the importance of prayer but didn't have a clue how to do it. I used to say to myself, "I don't get it, how do I actually pray? It sounds so comforting for people who do it, but . . . do I kneel and put my hands together? Or can I just sit?" This seems odd to me now. I now know it really is as simple as sitting and focusing my thoughts for a moment. For a long time, I had a hard time praying TO something or someone, and instead, I would just stop and breathe and say in my head, "I am so grateful for . . ." or "What is the right thing to do about this?" or "I'm praying for a happy, healthy day for my girls." I still do this every day. The existential questions as to what and who I'm praying to can be answered in time and are really only meaningful to me. It's the intent behind stopping to question, the release of positive thought and the gratitude that's important to me at this stage. Although, I still feel that declaring what I am grateful for to others goes further in utilising this valuable tool for wellbeing.

"Motherhood is tough. If you just want a wonderful little creature to love, you can get a puppy." — Barbara Walters

# Chapter Five

# Meditate

**Be mindful—without irony**

I remember being introduced to meditation in my early 20s, and to be brutally honest— just not getting it. I found the whole process annoying. My understanding was that the goal is to stop your mind from racing away with all the thoughts zipping around in it. I could not do that and, therefore, found it anything but relaxing. I also felt a bit self-conscious doing it and really couldn't see how it would help with much of anything.

In another episode of her podcast *The Happiness Lab* entitled "Calm Can Be Contagious," Dr Lori Santos interviews Dan Harris, an ABC News correspondent who, in 2004, had a panic attack live on TV. It seems his attitude to meditation at that time was similar to mine—he felt it was "for people who are really into aromatherapy and Cat Stevens and use the word Namaste with no irony". He goes on in the podcast to talk about what he has since learned about meditation and how it can be a valuable tool for mental, emotional and, indeed, physical wellbeing (Santos, 2020).

## The benefits of meditation

An article published on the health information site *Healthline.com* entitled "12 science-based benefits of meditation" lists the **enhancing effect on self-awareness** as an advantage of developing a meditation practice (Thorpe, 2020). This caught my attention while researching this book because many of the guiding principles I advocate are easily implemented through a change in what is most prevalent in our minds. The article points to existing research on how some types of meditation can lead to identifying destructive thought patterns. This awareness can then be used to steer the mind towards more constructive ways of thinking. This brings to mind my earlier examples of experiencing gratitude, nurturing community connections and being in the service of others as practices that could become second nature in thought through the practice of daily meditation.

Another well-researched benefit of meditation is thought to be its **reduction of the effects of stress,** and it's fair to say that motherhood is one of the most stressful human undertakings. I think most mums will have heard of cortisol—the hormone produced when a person is stressed. It's a very valuable function of our bodies and is designed to help us do whatever is necessary to get away from whatever is putting us in danger. Of course, as early humans, this was vital to keep us from being eaten by bears. But as I mentioned earlier with the sabre-toothed tiger example, sadly, we have not evolved at the rate society has, and so our bodies tend to display similar reactions to the stresses of our everyday lives as they would have done to meeting a bear in a forest many hundreds of years ago.

As *Healthline*'s article points out, cortisol produces inflammatory chemicals called cytokines. These chemicals can affect people in a whole host of negative ways, including disrupting sleep, increasing blood pressure and contributing to conditions such as inflammatory bowel syndrome and fibromyalgia. The article draws attention to an eight–week study published in the peer-reviewed literature publication *ScienceDirect* that found mindfulness meditation to be effective in reducing the inflammatory response to stress (Thorpe, 2020).

Staying with the physical benefits of meditation for a moment, in the 2020 episode "Calm Can Be Contagious" of *The Happiness Lab* podcast, Dan Harris points out an irony: Meditation—a practice most closely associated with Buddhism and part of what's required to attain enlightenment or "awakening"—has also been proven to **improve sleep**! One study identified by Healthline compared the different mindfulness-based meditations and found those who meditated "stayed asleep longer and had improved insomnia severity, compared with those who had an unmedicated control condition" (Thorpe, 2020). There are not many groups of people who can claim more sleep deprivation than mothers! If there is anything that can improve the quality of what little sleep so many mums tend to get, particularly in those early years of mumming around, then we should take it!

Meditation has also been proved through several different studies to **reduce levels of anxiety and depression**. To say motherhood within modern industrial societies can be stressful is an understatement. It's been estimated through a study published in the journal *Sociology*, which examined data from over 6000 participants, that full-time working mothers of two are 40% more stressed than working women without children (Chandola et al., 2019). A pretty scandalous statistic, and one we can do little about, given the social and economic climates in which so many of us are mothering.

And those pesky chemicals I mentioned earlier—cytokines—produced by the stress hormone cortisol–are thought to affect the mood and lead to negative thinking states like anxiety and depression. Thankfully, some studies have proved the effectiveness of meditation in combating these negative emotions. One study cited by *Healthline* found that those who practised a meditation exercise before viewing upsetting images experienced fewer negative thoughts as a result in comparison to other study participants in a control group (Thorpe, 2020).

There are other benefits to developing a meditation practice too. It's been proven to lengthen attention spans and help with memory loss, both of which are great improvements to make as busy mums with an eye on our long-term cognitive health and our roles as society's grandmothers. Is this the subject for a book in a few decades' time perhaps?!

**So, what is meditation?**

We've established the benefits of meditating. Now the question becomes, how do we get from somewhere around the mindset I was in for so many years about this strange Mideastern practice, to one where I don't only understand the benefits, but resonate so deeply with them that meditation becomes an unmissable part of my daily routine? I don't know the answer to that yet. There are still days when I allow life to get in the way. But two things I have come to understand that have helped me no end in this area are a), meditation is a practice—by which I mean an actual practice. I need to work at it to develop the skill in order to experience the benefits. And b), it really doesn't have to take up too much of my time.

So, how did I get started? There are so many videos and apps these days for learning how to meditate and being guided through meditation practice. It only takes a quick online search for "beginners' meditation" to be up and running. Along with the basics, which I've attempted to outline below (from the perspective of an interested party and not an expert), I have found it useful to keep one thing in mind as I meditate: not to get cross with my brain. As we've established, the chatter of the mind is an evolutionary tool for keeping us safe. It is doing its job. So, as my brain wanders during meditation, I try to think fondly of it as I keep coming back time and again to focus on my breathing. I thank it for trying to help and keep me safe and give it permission to stand down.

## So, what does it look like to meditate?

The first and perhaps hardest step to take as a mum, is finding some alone time and space: somewhere quiet. Easier said than done, right?! But there is always that moment just after lights out which you can take as a starting point. When Smalls are trying to fall asleep, mums are under no circumstances allowed to leave the room until that has been achieved! Once I have overcome this space and time hurdle, I make sure I'm comfortable. For me, that means having a bit of a shake-out before I start because I always seem to get fidgety just as I begin. Generally, I sit on the floor, with my legs crossed, my back straight and my hands on my knees. If sitting on the floor is too much, a straight-backed chair with my feet flat on the ground works perfectly too. The important thing for me is to be comfortable, and if that means the use of an extra pillow or even a cheeky lie down (which admittedly can incur the risk of falling asleep!), then so be it.

Once settled, it is time to close my eyes and start taking some deep, slow breaths. I focus on my breathing, choosing a nice, slow and steady tempo that's most comfortable for me. I find that's usually a four–to–five–count breath in, holding for a second and exhaling for four to five counts again.

The idea is to focus on the breath—the sensation of the air coming in and going out. Then, when the mind starts to wander and I notice that it has, I gently bring my focus back to my breath. The point is to keep bringing my mind back to the present moment and what is happening in it, which is quite simply that breath is coming in and out of my body. Dan Harris also talks about meditating as a skill—something we get better at the more we practice it. It takes time to start feeling the benefits, which are the ability to be more present in the moment and less reactionary to things happening around us. This, he says, is mindfulness (Santos, 2020).

Another thing Dan Harris talks about is something he calls "free-range" meditation. This is the idea that human beings can turn almost any activity into mindfulness access. He gives the example of when we wash our hands. We can pay attention to the "raw data" of that experience—the sensation of the water, the soap and how it feels both before and after it washes off. Trying to be more mindful in these experiences of daily life is a valuable meditation practice that can complement the development of formal practice.

## Tips for starting to meditate

It's important to mention that mindfulness meditation is not the only fruit here. Coming from Buddhism, it is probably the most familiar type of meditation and focuses on the breath, or an object, to bring the mind to awareness alongside a passive observation of thoughts, feelings or bodily sensations as outlined above.

There are, however, many other styles of meditation. Focused, spiritual, movement, visualisation, loving-kindness, transcendental, mantra and progressive relaxation, to name the nine most popular. It is important to **shop around** by looking into them and deciding which one seems most in tune with what's needed. All of them can be guided, and for me, this helps keep me focused on the practice.

One of the things that constantly gets in the way of my meditation is time. Or I should say, my belief that I don't have any. The great thing about meditation, however, is that it can be done **anywhere at any time** we are able to find peace and quiet. It need only be a minute if that is all we can find as busy mums. Personally, I only started to feel the benefits once I'd worked my way up to at least five minutes, but one minute following your breath during nap time, or before everyone else is awake in the morning, is better than no minutes at all.

Keeping our meditation practice **free from judgement** is key to developing the skill. That is the reason I try not to get cross with my mind when it wanders. Meditation is about noticing thoughts and feelings and observing them with compassion, as opposed to fighting or feeding them, as it's put by Dan Harris and Lori Santos in the "Calm Can Be Contagious" podcast episode on *The Happiness Lab*. If this is something we can start practising with more ease in our meditative practice, it's a way of being that will become more integrated with our lives in general.

Something I found helpful when starting to meditate was **recording my own voice** for guidance. I will say it felt a bit strange and self-conscious at first, but the idea is that I'm compassionately guiding myself into the mindful state and kindly reminding myself to stay aware. It's a great tool for applying a notion of self-love to the practice and so easy to do. There are many free guided meditation scripts available to use at the click of a button, and I have found it hugely comforting to nurture my inner child in this way.

"I believe the choice to become a mother is the choice to become one of the greatest spiritual teachers there is." — Oprah Winfrey

# Chapter Six

# Be curious and learn

### Curiosity improved the cat

"The whole of life, from the moment you are born to the moment you die, is a process of learning."

These are the words of philosopher, speaker and writer Jiddu Krishnamurti. He spoke extensively on philosophical issues such as consciousness and evolution, the nature of the human mind, psychological revolution, meditation, human relationships and bringing about positive social change. These days, I'm in total agreement with this great philosopher; I can't imagine a world where I'm not learning something new every day. But that wasn't always the case.

As a teenager and in higher education, I was something of an overachiever, bowling into the world of work with a degree, a masters and a diploma to my name. And at that point, I just stopped learning. It was as if I was all learned out. Of course, in reality, that wasn't true. Life began to teach me things. I learned how to do my job, I lived in Japan for a few years and learned to speak Japanese, I watched every medical drama around at the time and am oddly well versed (in an entirely amateur way) in the more dramatic class of medical ailments and approaches to curing them. But it seemed my curiosity was spent. The things I was learning were out of necessity or by osmosis, not because I actively sought them out.

Nowadays, it's a different story. My curiosity to understand things is constantly piqued. Take my interest in Jiddu Krishnamurti, for example. It was through research for this book that I came across him in detail, having only ever known vaguely who he was. The collection of writings and lectures about the individual in relation to society, entitled *Krishnamurti: Reflections on the Self*, is now on my book list (Krishnamurti et al., 2014).

It's not an exaggeration to say that being curious and learning has saved my life. OK, not literally. I have never been in a life-or-death situation where something I've picked up in a medical drama has come into its own. I'm talking more about my sanity. As a stay-at-home mum when my girls were very little, I would have gone slowly insane if it hadn't been for my curiosity to study and learn new things. I began to inhale audiobooks and podcasts, and can honestly say there hasn't been a day since I became a mum when I haven't learned one small new thing. And now, I discover there are actual scientifically proven wellbeing benefits to being curious! According to *Greater Good Magazine*, the online publication of The Greater Good Science Center at the University of California, Berkeley, curiosity has been linked to "psychological, emotional, social, and even health benefits" (*Greater Good Magazine*, 2015).

## The benefits of curiosity

Trying new things causes our brain to produce the feel-good chemical dopamine. Scientists tell us this is because exploring new things and gaining knowledge about the world around us is what **keeps us safe** and able to continue **evolving as a species**. The dopamine hit is, literally, the reward for taking action that will evolve us as a species, and it also has the knock-on effect of making us feel happier. Research shows us that curiosity is 'associated with higher levels of positive emotions, lower levels of anxiety, more satisfaction with life, and greater psychological well-being' (Campbell, 2015).

It seems fairly obvious that curiosity can also bolster **achievement.** I have found this to be the case personally. Something I am interested in—like the content of this book or my studies into how to improve my coaching skills—has always led to higher achievements in those areas. In a study into whether curiosity is the third pillar of academic performance after intelligence and effort, researchers led by Sophie von Stumm at Edinburgh University found that "a hungry mind" is a '"core determinant of individual differences in academic achievement" (von Stumm et al., 2011). Given that, as I've already pointed out, motherhood is a fly-by-the-seat-of-one's-pants learning experience, a curious mind and its support of achievement is a great thing to take into the journey.

Studies have also shown that people with a curious streak also display **greater levels of empathy** and **improved connections to others**. Being able to think about things from another person's viewpoint is going to increase the levels of empathy needed to make an enquiry of that person. One study found that people who ask questions and show genuine interest in the lives of others were "rated as warmer and more attractive" than those who don't (Campbell, 2015)—an advantage when another of the guiding principles that promotes wellbeing is nurturing community connections.

I see this with my Smalls all the time. When they are in the middle of frantic, seemingly illogical meltdowns, I take the time to show empathy; it almost instantly brings us back to a less emotionally charged and more connected state. I wait until they're calm and then show my curiosity as to what's really upsetting them. This is ten times more effective than when I just don't have time for a full-throttle tantrum and try immediately to shut it down.

This research into curiosity and learning has made me think a lot about my girls' questions as well—the constant whys and the questions I sometimes just can't find an explanation for. I learned early on to love their inquisitiveness (and to answer the fourth "Why?" with "What do you think?"). After all, it seems a child's ingrained level of curiosity and hunger to learn in part aids their development, keeps them safe and nurtures their potential for meaningful connections with others.

## Tips to keep curiosity and learning alive

Few people have less time than a mum. Gone are the days when we can pick up a book and sit for hours on end through a Sunday afternoon devouring it. But with advancements in technology (much of which I will lament in the next chapter) comes the advantage of being able to consume information on the go and in bite-sized chunks. And much of what could turn into a daily dose of learning something new will often come directly to our smartphones without us having to go looking for it.

**TED talks**, for example, have become a small part of my daily routine. They are a brilliant way to learn a good amount of information about a topic that interests me in a short amount of time. I started watching them right after my babies had fallen asleep while breastfeeding. That moment when the work is done, and mum can sit for a moment while baby settles into as deep a sleep as possible before the dreaded attempt to put them down . . . that was my time. These days, I try to watch one a day before I start my work.

And if not a TED talk, then there are also thousands of great **podcasts** out there. I try to find informative ones that also make me laugh. And the great thing about podcasts is that many of them have an interactive element where you can comment or write in as well. Obviously, the advantage to a podcast and, indeed, an **audiobook** over a TED talk is that they are often something you can listen to while multitasking with something else. I am never without something to listen to whilst grocery shopping, folding laundry or making dinner.

With podcasts and audiobooks so readily available online for free or with various subscriptions to different platforms, I wonder how many people know there are also many audiobooks available for free from the library. Quick sidebar: I recently discovered the power of listening to audiobooks in the car with the kids as well. I managed to find a story that really caught their imagination (and mine!), and suddenly, car journeys became peaceful and informative—another win-win for mumming around! End of sidebar. These days, I make it a goal to listen to at least one fiction and one non-fiction book a month. In reality, my listening rate is much higher, but that goal is achievable for those times when life is just moving too fast for me to take the time.

In my days before kids, I was a keen traveller. In fact, not simply **travelling**, but living in other countries for extended periods of time. One of my favourite things about travelling is that it satisfies my curiosity and means I'm learning about other places and cultures of the world. Personally, I have found keeping up with travel hard with kids, and that worried me in the beginning. What if I wasn't instilling in them a curiosity to get out and explore as I had? Then, I remembered they are very tiny. To them, going to a new soft play is akin to the kind of exploring I did in my early 20s and 30s. Travelling with kids is fab when it's feasible—if a little more stressful than travelling alone—but when it isn't, getting out and exploring new places, events and experiences is a great way to keep learning new things.

Interestingly, it didn't really occur to me to take courses or educate myself formally in the few years straight after finishing my education. Unless I had to study something for work, I operated under the idea that my studying days were over. I couldn't have been more wrong. Since becoming a mum, I have taken two **courses online** and gained so much from learning something new about subjects I am passionate about. I have also found that even just looking for courses online begins to spark interest in making changes in my life that are better aligned with my purpose. Becoming a coach was partly the result of pursuing online courses that had something to do with my interests at the time.

Another tip for staying curious is to find a **blog** or two to follow. This is a great way of letting info about something that interests you come your way because you can often sign up for notifications. Blogs frequently pull together information from other sources as well, so they can lead to gaining insight into other things that might be worth exploring.

Recently, I gave myself the challenge of learning **a new word a day**. This is not hard when you listen to a lot of podcasts and audiobooks. My word for the day at the time of writing this was "hegemony"—leadership or dominance, especially by one state or social group over others. (*Oxford English Dictionary*, 2022). So, while being curious to learn might feel like a thing of formal education, there is no reason it can't be part of mumming around life. As I've said, we are constantly learning how to raise our children, and that's not something anyone is ever formally educated in or tested on. Learning opportunities are everywhere in life. Even the writing of this book is a learning opportunity, and a curiosity satisfied every time I sit down to it.

"Motherhood has a very humanizing effect. Everything gets reduced to essentials." — Meryl Streep

# Chapter Seven

# Spend time in nature

**Let's go outdoors**

The wellbeing benefits of being outside in nature are increasingly becoming the focus of official psychological research, but I feel as though the idea that time connecting with the outdoors is a good thing has always been more or less undisputed in communal thought. I distinctly remember the day when I realised consciously what a positive effect being away from an urban landscape and surrounded by nature had on me. I'd been living in London for a little over 10 years and took a weekend break to the Lake District in North West England to do some walking. The first day, I remember saying over and over again in my head how much I missed the outdoors, how amazing I felt in the space and, of course, *I really must not leave it so long next time.* I was keenly aware of how much more peaceful I felt, just walking in nature (and for the most part in the rain that particular week) against the spectacular backdrop of lakes, mountains and rolling countryside. That day marked the start of a slow move out of an urban environment to a place where I now have access to that sense of peace in nature right on my doorstep.

Of course, it wasn't until recently that I read up on exactly *why* from a psychological standpoint, I found such a profound sense of peace that day. In a 2020 article written for the American Psychological Association's website entitled "Nurtured, by Nature", psychologist and behavioural analyst Kristen Weir looks at several studies on this topic. But she starts by asking her reader how much time they spend looking at a screen each day. It depends on which data source we look at, of course, but it seems the average daily screen time for people in Western society is believed to be between seven and 10 hours a day. Kristen Weir suggests this ever-growing reliance on technology, plus a trend towards urban living environments, is the reason human beings "are spending ever less time outdoors—even as scientists compile evidence of the value of getting out into the natural world" (Weir, 2020).

Studies have shown that exposure to green open spaces can enhance **cognitive development**. Memory function, attentional control and self-regulation are all known to have seen positive improvements and scientists have put forward a theory as to why that is: Since early man relied on the environment for survival, we evolved to form an innate connectedness with nature. One study even found that students who merely *listened* to the sounds of nature while performing cognitive tests performed better than their peers, who were listening to a more urban soundtrack (Van Hedger et al., 2018).

Weir goes on in her article to highlight several other studies that expose not only the cognitive benefits but also the **emotional advantages** of connecting with nature regularly. One of them was conducted on people in Denmark, by researchers who used satellite data to help them ascertain how much exposure people were having to green space throughout early childhood. They then compared this with data on mental health outcomes. There were more than 900,000 residents examined in this research, all of them born between 1985 and 2003. They found that children who were able to live in areas with more green space tended to have a lower risk of psychiatric disorders when they got older. This included substance abuse, eating disorders, mood dysregulation and depression. Children with less exposure to green space in early childhood had a 55% higher risk of developing a lasting mental illness (Engemann et al., 2019).

So, it seems the simple act of exposing ourselves to the outdoors can have an impact, not only on the functioning of our brains but on our emotional wellbeing as well. Spending time in nature can actively make us happier and more at peace.

## Tips for getting out in nature more

I'm lucky enough to have a garden. That's a privilege I don't take for granted. I'm even more fortunate to be able to see it from most of the rooms in my home, and I take a wander around it at least once a day, just to look, listen and breathe. That's something I have always done, since way before I started to understand the mental and emotional benefits of this seemingly innocuous undertaking. This is my way of ensuring I have spent at least a little bit of time outdoors every day.

Recently, however, I began taking more time to actually work in the garden. **Gardening** is a great way to spend time outdoors. Depending on what space is available, it can be anything from tending a few flowers in pots to tomato or strawberry plants to a small herb garden or, indeed, full-on flower displays and a veggie patch. I'm not green-fingered in any way, but what I lack in knowledge and, some might say, skill (and patience!), I more than make up for in enthusiasm and enjoyment. I only started doing any gardening after I became a mum and have found it to be such a great pastime for very many reasons. Firstly, things grow! So, even if I'm struggling to find the time to get out and tend to whatever it is I've planted (or left alone to grow from where it self-seeded!), there will come a point when I can't ignore that it needs some attention, which will force me outdoors. Secondly, I've noticed what a conversation starter it is with neighbours. I have one neighbour who is particularly green-fingered, with a huge and enviable cottage garden. Whenever I pop to see her, I get an hour-long wander around the garden, just looking and learning from her. The benefits of this are manyfold: It gets us both outdoors, it satisfies my curiosity and need to learn and it keeps me connected to my community.

Another way I make sure I'm getting some time in nature is to take a long walk as often as I can. I still belong to that walking group, which is ideal when I want to do a long walk but want the company of others, and to be guided on the route so I don't always have to be thinking about where I'm going. Walking has become my favourite way to get time in nature for myself.

## Tips for getting out in nature with the kids

Although this book is primarily about what guiding principles we can live by as mums to improve our own wellbeing, this, of course, becomes inextricably linked to the wellbeing of our children. I'd like to think I am modelling practice of the guiding principles I've talked about until now with my girls. Hopefully, they see how I try to be of service and connect with those around us. I have taught them about mindfulness and breathing and always encouraged their curiosity to learn. The tool of getting out into nature to promote wellbeing is a much less abstract concept for young Smalls to understand, however.

Since having children, time in nature has become a prerequisite of family life. I aim for it to happen every day, though it's not always possible. The weekends will usually involve at least one day outdoors. I have made a point of identifying as many places as I can near home where I can **walk in nature with the kids**. When I can, I will add activity to the walk. There are many books or hints and tips online for finding ideas to make walks fun. A quick search came up with the following list in under a minute: scavenger hunt, map reading, matchbox treasure collecting, cloud spotting, bark rubbing, gathering leaves and flowers for pressing, nature journaling, "Go find it" cards, penny walks (a flip of the coin determines the route!), nature bracelets (sticky tape round the wrist to stick things like leaves and feathers to), torchlit walks or an "I spy" hike.

The lure of a **play park** is also a sure-fire way to get kids out in nature. I have been known to incentivise walking with the promise of a play park at the end of it, but there is nothing wrong with a simple trip to the park to make sure kids are getting some outdoor activity time. There have been times when I've worried I'm not finding enough excitement for my girls in taking them to some of the same parks over and over again, but reflecting on this, I've noticed an unending capacity for my girls to have fun, even at parks they've been to thousands of times before.

**Picnics as a family** are another great way to get kids outdoors. Occasionally, I'll make this the whole day's activity, from choosing what food to take to making and packing up everything we need and finding somewhere to go. Again, this is the sort of thing that can be overlooked as a "fun thing to do" in a world where our kids are forever bombarded with so much fast-paced life content. But although I can't deny we have a few moans and groans when I'm asked, "What are we doing today?" and the answer is (with hands waving excitedly in the air) "It's picnic day!", I have noticed a real sense of calm comes over both my girls once we are out for that picnic.

**Gardening with kids** is also a brilliant activity to get us all connected to nature. The benefits of getting children interested in gardening are undisputed. A feature article on the website of the UK's leading gardening charity, the Royal Horticultural Society (RHS)—the place where I get most of my own hints and tips—points to research suggesting "children perform better at school if they're involved with gardening, and many will develop a greater interest in healthy eating if they get to grow their own veg." (*RHS* website, n.d.). The charity runs a school gardening campaign to get as many children in the UK involved as possible, on the basis that gardening helps develop a child's physical and mental wellbeing, an understanding of the environment and sustainability, confidence and self-esteem, teamwork and communication skills and literacy and numeracy skills (*RHS* website, n.d.).

## The importance of getting out in nature

I can't end a chapter about incorporating time outdoors as a guiding principle in a life geared towards improving wellbeing without mentioning Jenny Odell's book *How to Do Nothing*. With far more complex concepts and ideas than I can go into succinctly here, this beautiful book's main premise is about rejecting the 24/7 work culture encouraged by a capitalist narrative of productivity. Odell talks about how much is vying for our attention in modern life, not least via social media, and suggests a change in mindset where we are turning our attention to different things and looking at them in a new way to seek respite from what she terms "a crisis". In the book, she talks extensively about finding new ways of observing things in nature. It feels like the outdoors is primarily where she seeks solace for accessing this new way of paying attention. She writes, "I think it's a little bit unreasonable to stop paying a certain type of attention without suggesting another type of attention. So, for me, I started paying attention to ecology, specifically to birds." (Odell, 2020).

Anyone who has read this book will have gained a new appreciation of birds and what is available for noticing should we be able to turn our attention to them in a new way. After reading the book, I began doing something with my girls I hadn't done since they were tiny—I began encouraging them to notice things out on our walks. When kids are little, it feels instinctive to show them every beetle and piece of fungus along the way of a woodland walk. But when they get older and can walk further and climb trees—although, I think these are important activities too—the noticing of little things in detail starts to fall away.

In her article about Jenny Odell's book for *The Guardian*, Elle Hunt describes the author's notion of tapping into a mindset that directs attention differently as a kind of mindfulness; "the practice of simultaneously seeing more and zooming in with hyper-precision". This is something, Odell says, that gets easier with practice. Hunt quotes Odell, saying, "sometimes, it's the really simple thing of just asking, OK, what in this scene have I not noticed before?" (Hunt, 2020). I am now trying to do this often with my girls. We go on the same walks, but I remind them there is always something new to see if we look for it.

In an interview with the political commentator and former speech writer for Barack Obama, Jon Favreau, for his podcast *Pod Saves America*, Jenny Odell talks about how a friend of hers bought her a jeweller's loop and how it has become something she finds "endlessly fascinating" and full of wonder. She talks excitedly about how what is looked at through this little magnifying tool can be really surprising—something we might expect to look smooth, like the surface of a leaf that looks waxy to the naked eye, might actually be hairy and rough when viewed through the tiny lens. She compares the element of surprise and fascination it brings to the sensation we get when scrolling through social media—but without the dread (Favreau et al., 2022). I love the notion that we can find a way to tap into the emotional draw of what keeps us coming back to social media, without the element that is bad for our mental health. I also felt that a jeweller's loop is an incredibly inspiring way to start introducing children to the idea of looking at things differently and paying attention to what we don't see, as well as what we do.

"A mother's love for her child is like nothing else in the world. It knows no law, no pity, it dates all things and crushes down remorselessly all that stands in its path." — Agatha Christie

# Chapter Eight

# Spend less time on a screen

## Nobody wants square eyes

"To me, one of the most troubling ways social media has been used in recent years is to foment waves of hysteria and fear, both by news media and by users themselves. Whipped into a permanent state of frenzy, people create and subject themselves to news cycles, complaining of anxiety at the same time that they check back ever more diligently" (Odell, 2020).

This quote about social media from Jenny Odell's book *How to Do Nothing* got me thinking a lot about the amount of time mums spend on social media and what it's doing to our sense of wellbeing. It seems relatively undisputed that the sound bite, clickbait, and comparison culture of social media can have a negative impact on levels of **depression and anxiety.** What I've found as I've been researching this, however, is that it's less about social media per se and more about how it (and, indeed, anything digitally coming into our lives) is now instantly and constantly accessed through a device that many of us would now genuinely function less well without. Much in line with Odell's commentary about all the ways in which our attention is being pulled in different directions to create anxiety, researchers have found that even the *presence* of a phone (face down on the table or not) can subdue our enjoyment of whatever we're experiencing at the time.

Researchers from the University of Technology in Sydney, Australia, have reported there are 46 harmful effects of using some of the major social media sites like Twitter, Instagram, and Facebook on a regular basis. Since I'm sure you're curious, here are some of those effects listed:

Irritation
Stress
Panic
Depression
Guilt
Jealousy
Loneliness
Anxiety
Reduced self-esteem
Deterioration of mood
Self-dissatisfaction
Wasting time
Information overload
Addiction using social media
Wasting energy
Inappropriate posts
Wasting money
Offensive content
Work overload
Dumb jokes
Low job performance

Low academic performance

Delinquency

Being harassed

Conflicts with others

Incitement to suicide

Taking more financial risk

Being exposed to sexual things

Phishing risks

Malicious software

Poor content

Lack of privacy

Lack of online safety

Privacy violations

Misuse of information

Impersonation

Cyberstalking behaviour

Deception

Feeling of being abused

Researchers were able to come to this conclusion after looking through dozens of other studies on the negative effects of social media (Melore, 2021).

In another episode of *The Happiness Lab* entitled "Dial D for Distracted", Dr Laurie Santos draws our attention to what Steve Jobs said in 2007 at The Macworld Convention regarding the first-generation iPhone. He said, "Every once in a while, a revolutionary product comes along that changes everything" (Santos, 2020). He wasn't wrong. Santos points out how inattentive our brains are at the best of times, mentioning the now quite famous basketball/gorilla

*Selective Attention Test* [video] conducted by Daniel Simons and Christopher Chabris in 1999 (Simons & Chabris, 2010). For those who aren't familiar with it, this test asked participants to watch a video of six people throwing a basketball around and count how many times the players in white passed the ball. It's not hard to get the number right. But what many people don't notice the first time they watch is the man in a gorilla suit who walks across the frame directly through the middle of the players. The video is available to check out on YouTube and it's fun to see what you, or perhaps someone you know, notices the first time they watch it.

The original test proved to researchers that our brains are not wired to attentionally absorb everything our eyes see—there would simply be too much to process. Therefore, as Santos points out, if we want to use our limited attention on the things that make us happy and bring us peace, we first need to make sure we are directing our attention towards those things. And this, of course, is where our phones are not our friends.

It seems that more and more studies are being done on how the use of phones impacts our wellbeing. Santos highlights one study where participants were given a free massage while their phones sat at the side of the room. Half the participant's phones buzzed with a call halfway through the massage and, as a result, they reported significantly lower enjoyment ratings on a 9-point scale than those whose phones remained silent (Santos, 2020). It seems that what having a phone actually does is pull our attention out of moments we could be enjoying more mindfully, thereby **impacting our sense of happiness.**

This research got me thinking about how even the fact that I own a phone that is never far from my side might be affecting my own mental wellbeing and that of my children. Ironically, the very device that on paper has the ability to make me more connected to the outside world and, therefore, one might think, to the people in my life—my community—is actually having the opposite effect. A device that has the effect of taking me out of the moment, could in fact result in me feeling **less connected.**

In an article for the website *Very Well Family*, Katherine Lee speaks to James A. Roberts, Ph.D., professor of marketing at Baylor University and the author of *Too Much of a Good Thing: Are You Addicted to Your Cell Phone?*, to try to find out why this is so damaging. He states that "relationships are the cornerstone of our happiness, and, therefore, when we are being "phubbed" (the act of snubbing someone while engaged in your screen) the concept of being in a room with someone where that someone is virtually somewhere else entirely, is very conflicting to the sense of safety in the connection of that relationship" (Lee, 2021).

Lee goes on to list other ways in which too much phone use can be damaging. Research is beginning to show that smartphones can be as **addictive** as gambling, and they are also **contagious**. When one person "phubbs" another, that person's instinct is to simply get out their own phone and phub them right back. But probably, the most worrying way in which mums' (and, indeed, all parental figures') phone use is impacting society these days is that **Smalls are learning from their caregivers**. An acceptance that phubbing is a normal expected part of family life–along with increasing daily amounts of screen time–means children are changing the way they think and are able to entertain themselves.

## The benefits to minimising screen time

I should say at this point that not one of the people involved with the books or studies I've read and listened to on this topic advocates getting rid of phones—or even just social media apps—completely. There is a usefulness to having a smartphone which I feel would be counterintuitive to suddenly deny ourselves in this day and age, particularly given the hectic nature of our mumming around lives. But while it's becoming a commonly held belief that too much screen time of any sort is not good for children, I'm not sure it's as keenly acknowledged among adults that there are huge benefits to limiting our own screen time too.

Tearing ourselves away from our smartphones and other screens will result in **more engagement with those around us**—including our children. It will **improve our sense of wellbeing,** due to less exposure to what Jenny Odell claims is the "permanent state of frenzy" induced by social media these days. It will encourage us to think of other ways to **entertain ourselves** and our children. It might even result in **time freed up** for other tools and guiding principles to be deployed, such as gratitude, meditation, curiosity, and learning or exercise. It will also lead to better sleep. And ALL of these side effects of limiting screen time will be witnessed and, hopefully—in the long run—**modelled by our children**.

## Tips to limit screen time

One of the first things I did to limit my own screen time was to radically redesign my phone. I **moved all the social media apps** to my third screen page. The only apps that remain on my home screen are the ones I use to communicate with my girls' school or fellow mums, anything I use for work, including my calendar and, of course, my audiobook and podcast apps. I have also turned the **phone to greyscale** to make it less attractive, **turned off all notifications** and **use the wellness functions** on various apps and on the phone itself to keep me aware. Finally, I took a beautiful photo of my girls—wait for it—staged with them staring at phones. They are still little, and this image really jars with me. It's now on my home screen as a reminder that my phone use will become theirs.

In terms of a **more limited usage**, during the day, while I'm working—admittedly on a screen—I do have it with me. I make a conscious effort to only look at it once an hour to clear it, however. It is no longer something I am constantly checking on an ad hoc basis. **Mealtimes are screen free.** In the mornings, during breakfast, all screens are put away out of the room, and the same goes for dinner time. In the evenings, I make a point of not looking at my phone constantly and instead set aside half an hour to look at social media. These days, I don't even use the whole half hour and am much more inclined to plug into a book or a podcast. At night, the phone does not come to bed with me. It **charges up downstairs,** and I make a point of it not being the first thing I look at in the morning, opting instead for a daily affirmation card as my first thought for the day.

Where limiting phone and other screen use becomes tricky is where the phone's usefulness merges with family life. Online shopping, keeping in touch with the school, arranging the kids' activities, work, house admin—all these things are done via a screen, and it's hard not to find myself constantly drawn towards a screen to get things done without inconveniencing myself. I think what counts is

**awareness**—an awareness of time spent, an awareness of what I'm actually doing on said screen and an awareness that my children are watching.

## Tips to limit screen time for kids

Speaking of the kids and screens, different health organisations advise slightly varying parameters on this, but the generally recommended daily amount of screen time for kids aged five to 17 is no more than two hours a day *maximum*—preferably high-quality programming. I confess that in the past, we have occasionally slipped into having more than that, particularly on a weekend, and every time I get intentional about tighter limits, all I can think is *there goes my peaceful dinner-making time,* and *now I'm going to have to really get my craft on with them.* The idea that it will cost me in time for myself or time to get through a bit more of the never-ending to-do list has occasionally led me to relax screen time allowance. But I have realised now that these outcomes have so rarely been the case.

These days there are two precious times of the day when my girls are allowed to sit with their iPads. The first is predawn when they wake, and I feel like I have only just fallen asleep! I will give myself a few minutes to get up and into the land of the living, while they are allowed to snuggle onto the sofa and watch something. The second is that all-important time at the end of the day when I'm making dinner and getting other bits done—and they are still decompressing from their own days. It's a time of day when I feel we all need the downtime, and a screen remains my tool.

At the time of writing, managing my girls' screen time is, I'm sure, easier than it will be in years to come. But for now, some of what

I have put in place will, hopefully, set up good habits as they go forwards. Firstly, their screen time is **limited to two hours a day** maximum, without exception. We very rarely use that. But, for example, if we are going out for lunch where I know I will be grateful for half an hour's peace after the meal to enjoy a coffee, screen time then becomes factored into the day's allowance, and the morning's allotment becomes shorter to accommodate. We have a blanket consequence in place: Not coming off the iPad when asked will result in no iPad at all the following day. I only needed to follow through on this once (with much love and kindness, of course), and we haven't had a problem with it since.

Also, **their viewing is very restricted**. We have now settled on access to two TV and film-watching apps, and one games app. There is plenty for them to engage with, but they are never watching or playing anything I can't see or hear myself. That is another key thing for me. They have iPad time in the living room, very close to where I am. The iPads are never in their bedrooms (which, for us, are reserved for sleeping and dressing only), and the two hours before bed (minimum) are free from the screen.

The other thing I have done to help with limiting screen time is to make their **play area more accessible** to them (and it is a small area, not a big expansive room filled to the brim with toys they never play with). Together, we went through the toys and kept only what they truly love and what seems to engage them over and over again—lego, train tracks, skittles, dressing up stuff, toy food, puzzles, Jenga, books to read, plus arts & crafts/activity books. Their play area is somewhere they can walk into and easily decide what to do and access what they need. Too much choice can sometimes be paralysing, and this way, they are forced to find new games to play with simple toys they have had for a long time. It has been an eye-opener for me in what's needed to encourage imaginative independent play.

I can say without a shadow of a doubt that, although I still think all of us spend more time than is ideal looking into a screen rather than into each other's eyes, the small changes we have made at home have had a profound effect on the overall mood in our home. I will never stop trying to minimise exposure to screens and, more particularly, some of the activities engaged in through a screen that I feel are doing both adults and children alike a disservice in our modern world, but I concede also that there needs to be a balance. They are growing up in a tech-infested world, and to shield them (and myself) from it completely is also not the answer. The answer, of course, as always, is balance.

"Motherhood is not for the faint-hearted. Frogs, skinned knees, and the insults of teenage girls are not meant for the wimpy." — Danielle Steel

# Chapter Nine

# Minimise the clutter

**Tidy house, tidy mind**

Staying with the idea of minimising and decluttering what my girls have access to on their iPads and in their play area—these were not random acts of organisation on my part—they were founded in scientific research. In his TED talk *The paradox of choice*, which is also available to view on YouTube, psychologist Barry Schwartz talks about how the abundance of choice we are presented with in nearly every facet of life these days actually leads to us feeling more paralysed in our decision-making and ultimately affects our levels of happiness (*The paradox of choice*, 2006).

Schwartz makes the point that in Western industrial societies, we have come to believe that as much freedom as possible in life is the ultimate goal because freedom equals welfare. And it is a commonly held belief that freedom is an excess of choice, made possible by social, economic and technological advancements particular to the last number of decades.

Schwartz goes on to make the point that the amount of choice we now have has a negative effect in a number of ways. One is that we are almost paralysed by choice and end up unable to make a decision.

The second is that we end up less satisfied with the choices we DO make than we would have if we'd had fewer options to choose from in the beginning. He writes in his book, *The Paradox of Choice*, "Learning to choose is hard. Learning to choose well is harder. And learning to choose well in a world of unlimited possibilities is harder still, perhaps too hard" (Schwartz, 2009).

In his now infamous TED talk, he summarises these negative effects. He makes the point that the abundance of choice causes high expectations about how good the option we chose should be, so we are then predisposed to be disappointed with that choice. He adds that we then heap blame for both the inability to make a decision and the disappointment it brings onto ourselves. We have come to feel that with so many choices available to us, it is a failure on our part if we don't do it well. Schwartz claims that a significant contributor to the explosion of clinical depression in the last generation is down to this phenomenon (*The Paradox of Choice*, 2006).

Schwartz also states there is a point where we experience the advantages of having a choice—in contrast with "the good old days", when there was only one telephone provider or style of jeans. He also points out, however, that he has no idea where it is that the pendulum swings from a greater choice being beneficial to it being a hindrance. Though he is fairly sure we have long since passed it as a society (*The Paradox of Choice,* 2006).

In a study published in the online social and natural science journal *Nurture Human Behavior* about the effect of choice overload on the brain, participants were asked to make decisions while in an MRI machine, so brain activity at that time could be monitored. Volunteers were given a selection of landscapes they could have printed on a souvenir. They were split into groups. One group was to choose from six options, a second from 12 and the last from 24 scenes. Scans showed activity in two parts of the brain at decision-making time. First, in the anterior cingulate cortex, where we weigh the costs and benefits of any decision. And secondly, in the striatum, where we determine value.

Brain activity was highest when the subjects had 12 options to choose from. This led researchers to conclude that 12 seems to be the sweet spot when it comes to the optimal number of choices for making a decision. This also shows us the idea that some choices are good, but not too many. If you have too many choices, it is too hard to make a decision, but if you don't have enough options, then you may feel cheated (Reutskaja et al., 2018).

This idea that too much choice is a bad thing really resonates with me. So much so, that research into the idea led me to find Courtney Carver, the creator of a beautiful website called *Be More With Less* and writer of the book *Soulful Simplicity*. She came to create these things after a serious health scare and the search for a life that would help her find "the space, time, and love to be more me" (*Be More With Less* website, 2022). In the intro to her website, Carver asserts that by 'focusing on the best things instead of all the things, you can create a life with more savings and less debt, more health and less stress, more space and less stuff, and more joy with less obligation' (*Be More With Less* website, 2022). For the last year, I have made a conscious effort to minimise the choices I have to make daily. Happily, I now have a wardrobe where well over 50% of it is worn on a weekly basis. I no longer have a difficult decision to make each morning when deciding what to wear, and this radical (by some people's standards!) move got me thinking about clutter in the home in general . . .

I'm sure most mums can relate to the feeling of walking through the house and finding clutter everywhere. It's unsettling. Conversely, when I take the time to go through a cupboard and have a clear out—or even through my inbox, to get a little more organised with life admin—the sense of accomplishment comes with a heady mixture of joy and relief. There are now countless articles and scientific studies focused on the negative effects of clutter in the home. Some have found that, particularly for women, too much stuff in the home can lead to increased and unabating levels of cortisol throughout the day. Other studies have found that an untidy home can even lead to patterns of harmful behaviour such as unhealthy eating, binge-watching TV and sleeping poorly. In short, clutter can negatively impact mental wellbeing.

### The benefits of decluttering

The more I read about this topic, the more I realise my attack on clutter has positively impacted my overall sense of wellbeing.

I have definitely benefited from having more **clarity and focus**. I am almost always able to find things these days. I would also say I am better able to stay on top of life admin because the task of locating and sorting through the sheets of paper thrust at me as I collect the girls from school or the post that comes tumbling through the door with all the junk mail (which gets immediately binned!) is much less onerous.

Decluttering is said to help develop **higher self-esteem**. Granted, this is no scientific study, but when I think about the areas of my house I have decluttered and compare them to those still on the to-do list, there is a definite sense of ease and accomplishment around the former—and a sense of unease around what's still left to sort through.

I have also read that living in a decluttered home **improves relationships.** This is easy to understand if we apply the raised cortisol levels associated with women who feel their homes are messy and disorganised. I am often able to pinpoint being snappy and on edge to a connection to feeling overwhelmed by mess. So, it stands to reason that this would affect how I show up in relation to others.

**Reducing allergies and asthma** is a fairly obvious side effect of decluttering the home. The fewer objects there are, the less opportunity for dust to settle and the easier it is to clean.

I have seen a tangible improvement in my overall wellbeing as a result of decluttering in my life. I have extended this from my wardrobe out to each room in the house, onto the food I buy and prepare for meals, to the things I attempt to achieve on any given day, and even to my mind, through journaling and meditation. I am pretty keen on decluttering most aspects of my life—anything that makes it feel less full and more manageable is a win in mumming around for me.

## Tips for keeping clutter to a minimum

There are experts in this field with advice around detailed and extremely clever ways of decluttering life. Not least the aforementioned Courtney Carver. But as a starting point, here are a few of the tips I've implemented.

**Take it one room at a time.** As busy mums, we are unlikely to be able to tackle the house all in one go (blissful though the idea of a few days on our own to get back on top of things might sound!). I genuinely took on my house, one room at a time. With each room I created a ruthless sell or throw pile and designed it so that everything left had a place. I have already mentioned my wardrobe. I think the limits of it now would shock some of my friends! I have very few outfits I don't wear, and only a handful of shoes for each season. The result has been extremely liberating.

**Clean and tidy on the go**. This may sound like cleaning for dummies, but it works. More than ever since becoming a mum, I seem to spend my life moving things from where they've been left to where they should go—or asking my girls to do it. Sometimes, I marvel at the fact I always seem to be tidying, but I know if I don't, the task will become overwhelming very quickly. Recently, I found myself calling for Ida, my eldest, who was up in her room pootling about. We were late and, eventually, I climbed the stairs to see what she was up to. I found her straightening some teddies on a beanbag in her room. "All OK?" I asked. "Yeah," she answered, "just tidying up so I don't have to do it later because I want to do watercolours when we get home." *Boom!* There have, of course, been times when I've suggested we leave the mess and just have fun. I want both my girls and I to be OK with a bit of chaos from time to time too. But the idea of generally tidying as we go certainly makes the task of keeping the environment less overwhelming much less daunting to tackle when the time comes.

**Experiences rather than stuff.** One year, when my girls were little, I threw a whole class party for their birthdays. Never mind that the stress (not to mention the expense) of it nearly wiped me out, but essentially, what we ended up with was a lovely memory for the girls and thirty more things for each of them to fit in the play area. The gifts were beautiful, and so generous. I remember thinking how lucky they were. Until I walked through the play area one day and suddenly felt so overwhelmed on their behalf. It was bursting with "stuff"! It struck me that those memories could be made just as easily with the money being spent on a small experience with family or a few friends. The stuff, while nice, just wasn't necessary.

**Streamline the schedule**. I have taken to reducing the amount we try to achieve as a family each week. The extracurricular activities it seems we're expected to fill our kids' lives with and the activities we feel obliged to spend money on and ferry them around to appear to be at record levels. I have reduced everything down to much more manageable levels and frequently find myself at home with my girls with "nothing" to do. I have to admit, I used to be scared of days like that. The hours of "boredom" stretched out ahead of me, where I was expected to think of ways to stimulate the minds of two small humans.

How wrong I was. It is not my job to entertain them. I have noticed a marked difference in my girls' abilities to entertain themselves. There's an acceptance that they must find something to do together if I'm unavailable to facilitate the play. The first time I heard my eldest say to my youngest, "OK, choose a book and I'll read it to you", I welled up with the realisation that what I have actually done is give them back the agency to find their own entertainment. As Courtney Carver puts it, "Simplicity doesn't change who you are, it brings you back to who you are" (Carver, 2017).

**Simplify the food.** As part of my decluttering crusade, I pulled apart my kitchen and my weekly shopping list to reduce the number of options there are for meals and snacks. The food in the house is still balanced and nutritious, but rather than five different cereal choices or sandwich fillings, there are now only two or three. I also began shopping in places where I know the choice between brands is more limited. My experience of shopping and preparing meals has become quicker, simpler and altogether more efficient, and my girls have barely even noticed.

**Minimise the to-do list.** I recently went through my to-do list and ruthlessly deleted anything I didn't *really and truly* need to do for my own wellbeing or that of my family. To my surprise, I almost halved it. There is no honour in putting things on that list that won't necessarily have any benefit to anyone I love, which I just won't have time for and that will, therefore, only cause me to not meet my own expectations. Nobody will remember me for the things I never got around to, so why not take them off the list entirely? The very act of doing this also had the knock-on effect of clearing the decks of my mental load—a not insignificant and beneficial decluttering of a different sort.

**Declutter the mind.** Of course, the act of keeping lists can help with clearing space in the mind. When I am not trying to hold everything in my head because I know there is a list I can refer back to, I am infinitely more at peace. But decluttering the mind is also, for me, one of the goals of journaling and meditation. I have come to notice the power of sharing my thoughts around something that's bothering me (or indeed, exciting me), and in the absence of a human being to do that with, I will often turn to a review journal to transfer that chatter from my head to the page. And for me, meditation is similar, not necessarily in getting rid of the thoughts, but in releasing me from the attachment to them that can make the mind feel very overwhelmingly full at times.

In her book *Project 333: The Minimalist Fashion Challenge That Proves Less Really is So Much More*, Courtney Carver says this: "There is so much we can't control about how fast things are moving, so it's even more important to slow down the spaces and places we can. Simplifying things will help. Eliminating things will help. Less will help" (Carver, 2020).

I have become a huge fan of decluttering life. The effects on my sense of physical, mental and emotional wellbeing are palpable. Long may a life of less be so much more!

“The fastest way to break the cycle of perfectionism and become a fearless mother is to give up the idea of doing it perfectly – indeed to embrace uncertainty and imperfection.” — Arianna Huffington

## Chapter Ten

# Get more quality sleep

**Sleep like your babies**

I honestly can't remember the last time I got more than five to six hours of unbroken sleep in one night. I just don't have those children. The phrase "sleep like a baby" has taken on a whole new meaning since having kids. In reality, in my world, this would mean finding someone I could wake every night around midnight to retrieve my drink, take me to the toilet or allow me to recount my dream to—before, of course, insisting they sleep next to me with my foot or hand resting across their face.

Wakeful nights are an uncontrollable entity in my mumming around life, and they always have been. But there are things I can do to mitigate the harmful impact of being constantly sleep-deprived and understanding the importance of getting good shuteye has been my first step.

In an article for the Sleep Foundation entitled "How Sleep Works: Understanding the Science of Sleep", Eric Suni outlines the basics. Comfortingly, as I revisited this research some half a decade after I could often be found googling "baby sleep, what's normal?!" in those early days, much of what I read in this article was still familiar to me!

Essentially, there's a lot more going on than we might think when we sleep. Although our heart and respiration rates reduce, our body temp cools and our brain activity slows, as we go through the stages of sleep, our bodies and brains take time to recuperate. While this recuperation is happening in the body and brain throughout all the stages of our sleep cycle, on a basic level, it's believed the third stage of sleep, which is the deepest, plays an important role in our body's recuperation. The fourth stage is essential for regenerating our brain's memory and learning function (Suni, 2022).

Suni goes on to list the negative impacts of not getting enough sleep, including heart problems, mental health issues such as depression and anxiety, a weakened immune system and the risk of developing type 2 diabetes or becoming obese. Given how damaging a lack of decent sleep can be to physical, mental and emotional wellbeing, it is essential to acknowledge its "contribution to the proper functioning of nearly all of the systems of the body" (Suni, 2022) and to resist what, in my view, has become most Western industrial societies' lack of respect for its importance. The Sleep Foundation recommends that adults get between seven and nine hours of sleep a night, but reports that 35.2% of all adults in the U.S. are sleeping on average for less than seven hours per night.

As mums, it's also important to understand there is a gender sleep gap. A study presented to the American Academy of Neurology's annual meeting in 2017 found that *only* 48% of mothers under 45 years old reported getting at least seven hours of sleep per night and feeling tired more often than their childless contemporaries. No link was found between how long men slept and the presence of children in the house, leading researchers to support previous conclusions to similar studies that claim there is a gender sleep gap between men and women

("Living with Children May Mean Less Sleep for Women, but Not for Men," n.d.).

## Tips for getting better sleep

These findings, coupled with the knowledge of how important sleep is for physical, mental and emotional wellbeing make getting a decent amount of quality sleep one of the most important tools we can employ in mumming around life.

There are a million articles out there about creating healthy sleep habits, and let's face it, as mums, many of us learned them early on in our mumming around lives while setting up good sleep habits for our babies. It's instinctive to lower the light in a room where you're trying to settle a baby at night, and most new mums learn about the effect of the vacuum cleaner's white noise very early on! Over the years, I've become more and more interested in the science of sleep, and although most of what I've learned seems to be common knowledge among many of my fellow mothers, I often find I forget to practise what I've learned myself. I can slip out of good habits at the drop of a hat.

So, here is how I handle sleep by way of a reminder, not least to myself!

I make sure I get **exposure to natural light** early on in the day. I have read it is part of what helps align our sleep-awake rhythm. I don't find this hard now I have Smalls because they are little alarm clocks who, I find, also really benefit from getting out of the house—even on our lazy days when there is no school run to force us out into the world.

Obviously, another hindrance to both falling asleep and maintaining quality, sound sleep is the intake of stimulants. **Limiting caffeine, alcohol, nicotine and other stimulants** such as some medications will help in promoting healthy sleep. There was a time when I could drink coffee in the morning and still fall asleep in the evenings, but these days, any caffeine at all is a no go. The same goes for alcohol and other stimulants, which I now stay away from for many reasons, not least my quest to be as fresh-faced as possible while mumming around!

I have also found that following advice around a **sleep schedule** and a **bedtime routine** has helped me maximise my sleep. I have read that aiming for a typical daily routine—around all activities, including meals, as well as the time I get up and go to bed, is beneficial to getting a decent night's sleep. This isn't possible every day because life gets in the way, but as a mum, when the general consensus seems to be that children thrive on a routine, I am easily able to set one up for myself as I'm planning for them. I tend to wake and sleep at the same time and eat meals at the same time. I also stick to a predictable bedtime routine, which—as so many mums know works for kids—signals to my body that it's almost time to sleep and helps it to start preparing for that.

Part of both mine and my girls' routine involves **avoiding screens** for at least two hours before sleep. Most people these days understand the wakeful effect of the blue light that's emitted from screens and stimulates our brains. But this light can now be turned off on most devices and, of course, that's not the only thing that stimulates the brain when it comes to screen time. As we've already explored, mental overload and the links between the social media we are consuming on those screens and anxiety or depression, also provide a compelling argument for turning them off close to bedtime.

As I mentioned, I have recently taken to charging my phone and other devices out of the bedroom as well. There was a time when my phone would sit on charge next to the bed all night. But now, keeping it elsewhere is all part of creating a **good sleep environment**. Obviously, a decent mattress, pillows and bedding are part of that too. But what I didn't realise until I had children was how light, sound and smell can affect sleep as well. These days I only have red or amber lighting on in the evenings, which I try to reduce to no light at all for sleep time. If my girls need a night light, they have small red plug-in lights that emit just enough of a red spectrum glow to comfort them when they wake up. We all sleep with white noise on, and I have an aromatherapy diffuser on for a little while before we sleep.

The other advice I follow around sleep is to get up for 20 minutes if I can't nod off and do something else. Usually, this involves moving to a chair and reading a few pages of a book. I have started making a conscious effort not to do things in bed like eat and watch TV or scroll on my phone. In a page outlining its tips for better sleep, The Sleep Foundation states, "as a general rule, use your bed only for sleep and sex. Try not to eat, watch TV, study, or work in bed," and I have found that following this advice does contribute to an easier time falling (and staying) asleep (Florendo, 2022).

The Sleep Foundation also points to getting at least **20 minutes of exercise a day and eating well** to aid healthy sleep. Studies have found a link between nutritional deficiencies and poor sleep. It seems that sleeping, eating and exercising are well interlinked and essential to maintaining physical (and, in part, mental and emotional) wellbeing. If one of these elements is not on point, the others will suffer. When I'm eating nutritiously, my exercise and sleep will improve. When I'm sleeping well, I find it easier to exercise and make healthy food choices. When I'm exercising, I see improvements in the way I eat and sleep. With exercise and nutrition, which we will explore in the next chapter, I feel I have a lot of the answers; I just find it hard to put them into practice. Sleep was something I never really paid much attention to, however. It is also the thing that is most often sabotaged by something outside my control—namely, the sleep patterns of my children. Finding there are a few small changes I can make to my routine and my sleep environment that will give me a fighting chance at a decent night's sleep has been a game changer in my mumming around life.

"Thus far the mighty mystery of motherhood is this: How is it that doing it all feels like nothing is ever getting done." — Rebecca Woolf

# Chapter Eleven

# Eat well

### Relationship with food

Hands up in the room if you know what is and isn't good nutrition? Do you know how to fuel your body, but often get to the end of the day having consumed too much of the food you know won't do you any good? To an extent, that is probably most human beings at one time or another these days. We eat for comfort as well as for fuel. When I was growing up "comfort eating" had negative connotations. Since having children, I have started to see it differently. Comfort eating is inevitable; I learned this when breastfeeding both my girls. Babies often feed for comfort and not simply nutrition. They feed to connect with mum for reassurance, to relieve pain when teething, to calm down if upset or to regulate their temperature. Getting to the breast is the most basic human need at birth alongside physical safety. So, it began to come of little surprise to me that when I need comfort as an adult, I look to food.

Sadly, I feel there are many, many forces at work in modern industrial societies that can result in our relationship with food becoming unhealthy. In a society where mental unwellness has been steadily on the rise for many years, it seems obvious that eating for reasons over and above fuelling of the body will also have increased. Then, there is the abundance and availability of food that we live with these days. No longer is finding and preparing food the same effort it would have been many hundreds of years ago, and this can't fail to have led to excessive and overly frequent eating in some people. Add to this the food industry and its drive to sell cheap, processed food that looks very little like actual food at a molecular level, and I can understand why so many people begin to find themselves overweight or suffering with other conditions related to the food consumed. In my case, this in turn led to an even more unhealthy relationship with food–particularly when faced with societal norms about how my body was supposed to look. This culminated in the stark realisation that I have suffered with disordered eating all my life.

I am, thankfully, now in recovery mode. This is to say, I understand there is an issue and work every day to overcome it. Understanding what is at play began with me understanding my history with food—something I suspect many people will be able to relate to on some level. My first memory of issues with food and my body goes back to when I was 8 or 9. Life presented me with a very clear understanding that being overweight was bad. I knew early on what was considered beautiful. I also understood I was not sporty and petite. I was "heavy-boned" and felt slow and dumpy. Looking back, I had a strong sense, which I was never able to put into words, that I simply took up too much space in the world.

By the age of 12 I was obsessed with two things—dieting and eating. I can't remember a time until recently when I haven't constantly thought about what I was going to eat next or what I was going to do to lose weight. A pattern emerged where I would eat fairly balanced and nutritious (though quite restrictive) meals throughout the day, but they would be supplemented by heavily processed carb snacks, and by the evening I'd have, therefore, given up on the diet. Then I'd go nuts at dinner time with the 'blown it now, might as well go all out' mentality, and end up going to bed with a tummy ache. At 30, I was diagnosed with a bowel disease called Ulcerative Proctitis, which led to even further confusion around food because there were now foods which I knew triggered my symptoms, but of course, they were the ones I craved.

Having children was the catalyst for a creeping realisation that I had an issue with food. This was another way in which an element of mumming around has helped me to find a sense of peace and happiness. I realised I was practising a sensible, measured way of feeding my girls, which included little tips such as eating consciously as much as possible, not resorting to offering unhealthy snacks to cheer them up, and, obviously, trying to provide and teach them a balanced and nutritious way of eating. At the same time, I was practising so little of that myself in my own eating habits.

I began to feel I was going insane. And that really is the right word for it. My disordered eating was an issue of the mind, not of the body, and after a lot of soul searching and research, I found myself in recovery and taking steps to alleviate the emotional unwellness I was experiencing that caused me to use food in an unhealthy way. Much of that practice is outlined in the pages of this book. It's about being of service to others, connecting with community, practising gratitude, meditating and satisfying a thirst to keep learning. It's about limiting activity that harms the soul, such as comparing myself to others, and practices that go against connection and service, like joining in with gossip. In short, living better, makes me eat better.

## Education around food

I also have a nutritionist who has taught me some of the basics of healthy eating that apply to what my body needs to make it run at optimum health. I think a few of the things she has taught me apply to most people universally. Firstly, **sugar is bad**. It's unlikely that many people still don't know the risks of eating too much sugar, which include heart and liver disease, type 2 diabetes, high blood pressure, obesity, acne and tooth decay. Apparently, there is only one type of sugar the body actually needs, and that's glucose. The body makes glucose for itself at the levels it needs when breaking down some carbohydrates, proteins and fats. Any other added sugar is over and above what the body needs to function, and it seems to be in almost everything. I personally try to stay away from the large quantities of sugar found in very sweet fruits and simple carbs like white flour and white rice. But what I avoid like the plague is any added sugar—whether manufactured (like sugar in cookies and cakes) or naturally occurring (like when honey is added to cereal bars, for example).

The second thing my nutritionist taught me is: **processed food is bad, whole food is good**. This is mainly because heavily processed food often contains added sugar, salt and fat. But also, they are often stripped of their nutritional value while being processed and contain lots of artificial ingredients. Small amounts of processed food are often very calorific but are digested more quickly by the body than whole food, causing us to crave more, very quickly after eating. Most worryingly, however, a study published by *The BMJ* (formerly known for over a century as the *British Medical Journal*) found a direct link between an increase in the consumption of ultra-processed foods and a higher risk of cancer (Fiolet et al., 2018).

Essentially, however, the most important thing I learned from my amazing nutritionist is that it's vital to **educate ourselves about food and how it affects our bodies**. It feels absurd when I think back to the ignorance with which I used to fuel my body—often inefficiently and, in many cases, harmfully—when it is surely one of the most important things we can do for ourselves in life. Educating myself on how I can do better also fits nicely with the guiding principle of staying curious to learn. My learning has led me to adopt a more whole-food, plant-based way of eating, although I do still eat a little dairy and other animal products. I try to eat more protein and fewer simple carbohydrates than I used to, and endeavour to stay away from processed food. All stimulants such as alcohol, caffeine and sugar are off the table for me. After years of playing around with my food, my current way of eating, though not set in stone, is one I find regulates my mood, has me sleeping better, sees me exercising more and generally feeling more energised and well.

## Tips for eating well

Sadly, it's not just about education. Being a mum can make it really hard to follow what we know is a great way of eating for ourselves. In recent years, I have developed a number of strategies to help me stay on track. The first and most important is to **cut myself some slack**. I have one of those all-or-nothing brains. I'm either doing everything perfectly (according to my own standards!) or throwing caution to the wind and cutting off all communication with the little voice inside my head that's saying *perhaps that's not the best thing to be eating right now*.

But when I stop giving myself a hard time, that's when I tend to make better and more rational choices.

For me, another key to staying healthy and nutritious with food, as I described earlier, has been adopting the guiding principle of **decluttering around food choices**. For some reason, this just works for me. I keep the variety of food in the house quite minimal and rarely have a plethora of unhealthy snacks to choose from when I feel peckish. This also makes mealtimes easier in that I don't have to spend any time deliberating over what to cook. It may sound boring, but there are plenty of opportunities in life for me to eat the more varied foods I don't have as part of my core way of eating at home. And like I said, I have found this strategy makes food shopping quicker and easier too.

I also find **meal planning** (and where I can, meal preparation) at home invaluable to sticking with a particular way of eating. When I'm making breakfast and packed lunches in the morning, I tend to make part or all of what I will eat for the day, so that when it comes to mealtimes, there is little to think about other than going to the fridge to get it. Batch cooking at the weekends will also serve to help with this planning, as will keeping convenience eating (going to the drive-through or eating out) to an infrequent treat, as opposed to every other day.

For a long time now, I have also consistently used **smaller plates** at home by way of ensuring portion control. There was a time when I'm certain I would routinely eat twice as much as was necessary at mealtimes. The idea of using smaller plates has been around for years and, for me, it is now the norm. If what I'm eating doesn't fit on a side plate, then I'm eating too much.

Whilst researching healthy ways of eating for myself over the years, I have come across countless pieces of advice and experts championing a variety of different food plans (and I have tried most of them). Add this plethora of conflicting advice to the food industry's primary goal of making money, irrespective of the harm it may do to the people actually buying the food, and this whole aspect of life—how to effectively fuel the body—can feel overwhelming, to say the least.

During my research, I came across Dan Buettner, a National Geographic Fellow and explorer whose work has involved identifying and writing about what he calls "Blue Zones". These are five places in the world identified as home to people who live the longest and most healthful lives. He found the people in these communities had several things in common promoting their longevity. They valued and nurtured strong social and family ties, they didn't smoke, their diets were low in animal products and high in whole plant foods, and they enjoyed consistent and moderate physical activity such as gardening, riding their bikes to work, and occasionally, more formal and intentional forms of exercise. He writes of his findings in *The Blue Zones: 9 Lessons for Living Longer from the People Who've Lived the Longest,* and says about one of these communities, "They exercised mindlessly, by just gardening, walking to their neighbour's house, or doing their own yard work. The lesson to us: Engineer more mindless movement into our lives by living in neighbourhoods with sidewalks, owning a bike that works, and planting a garden each spring" (Buettner, 2012).

"Motherhood isn't a typical love story, it's the raw unedited version with all the outtakes, which is what makes it the most beautiful love story of all." — Jessica Urlichs

## Chapter Twelve

# Exercise enough

**Get moving!**

Exercise! It's the nemesis of many mums desperately trying to stay healthy alongside carrying out the time-poor and completely over-capacity role of motherhood. I've never had a great relationship with exercise. As I've mentioned, I've always felt heavy-boned and lacking in the energy required to motivate myself—I was definitely no Sporty Spice—Scary perhaps, but not Sporty. Motherhood exacerbated this feeling, of course. In those early years, I was the heaviest I've ever been, exhausted from the sleep deprivation and just couldn't see a spare moment in the day when I could fit in the simplest of tasks like showering, let alone going for a run.

Naturally, this was part of the problem. With that "all-or-nothing" mentality at work, I'd got it into my head that unless I worked my way up to being able to run 10k at the drop of a hat and then did it five times a week without fail, then what was the point? So, I convinced myself that exercise just wasn't something I could factor into life at that time.

The World Health Organisation recommends at least 2.5 to 5 hours of moderately intensive—and 1.5 to 2.5 hours of vigorously intensive—aerobic activity a week for adults. It also recommends muscle-strengthening activities and further aerobic exercise to achieve additional health benefits. I would hazard a guess that many mums are, sadly, nowhere near these proportions despite the numerous health benefits that come with exercising in these quantities (*World Health Organisation* website, 2022).

Getting enough exercise improves sleep, reduces stress and regulates emotions. It also keeps the body fit for purpose, avoids injury and prevents other life-limiting health conditions. A study published in *The BMJ* that investigated associations between physical activity and the risk of diabetes, heart disease, strokes and cancers such as breast and colon concluded that "people who achieve total physical activity levels several times higher than the current recommended minimum level have a significant reduction in the risk of the five diseases studied" (Kyu et al., 2016). That's a pretty compelling argument for getting more exercise, certainly way more than I was getting in those early years of motherhood.

The last few years have been something of a reformation for me in the way I view exercise. I am not an inactive person. With a strong (and some circles of thought might say unhealthily focused) productivity driver, I am not one for lounging around. And there have been periods of time throughout my life when I've glimpsed the joy that "being sporty" can bring. So, getting over the lack of energy and time, plus my all-or-nothing attitude seemed like an imperative nut to crack.

**Tips for getting more exercise**

Of course, improving my sleeping and eating habits took care of the energy issue almost overnight. The all-or-nothing attitude proved a little harder to reconcile with, but then I remembered Dan Buettner's "mindless" comments. And I have come to embrace and love the idea of **mindless exercise.** For me that is working in the garden. I was shocked to discover what a toll that can take on the body (in a really feel-good way). There are probably one or two changes we can all make to our daily way of life that would start to incorporate some mindless exercise where it didn't exist before. Even walking instead of using transport where possible for one or two journeys a week would be a great start.

That's not to say I haven't also managed to get some intentional, formal exercise into my day as well. Like incorporating all the tools and guiding principles I'm trying to live by or use in my day-to-day life, the key has been to make it **part of the daily routine**. My morning now takes care of vigorous exercise and is done by the time we are out of the door for the school run. I won't pretend there aren't times when I just can't be bothered, but I do it anyway because I can't now "unknow" the importance of it. This also has an added advantage. It happens in front of my girls, and role models how normal it is to make exercise a part of life. We have also made a large component of our free time activity centre around exercise, and they know we will do at least one long walk every weekend and one yoga session during the week as a family. Again, two small changes to our week that will have an impact on our collective health.

Another thing I have done that helps with incorporating more exercise into my daily life is to **keep it simple**. There is nothing more effective than my brain's ability to locate obstacles when I just don't feel like doing something. So, I pre-remove anything that can get in the way of a workout or mindless activity. One of the things that used to stop me from working out, for example, was not having the equipment or the ability to take time away from the girls. I used to tell myself things like, "Well, if I had a running machine, I would work out, but I don't, and I can't get out for a run regularly because I can't leave the girls so, oh, well . . ." Now, I do a workout that needs no equipment—with the girls in the room. I make sure I have my clothes and water bottle standing by in the morning so getting started is as easy as possible. Looking back, I am impressed with the number of hurdles I could put in my way if I tried hard and really didn't want to exercise!

Finally, with that old productivity driver at play in almost everything I do, I now get a kick out of figuring out how I can **multitask** in this activity. I work out to a timer and do a routine I now know like the back of my hand. This means I can listen to a book or podcast and learn something at the same time. Obviously, mindlessly exercising while gardening has the added advantage of getting me out in nature and checking off the tool of that daily wellness practice in the process. I have even started playing around with walking meditation.

So, we can say there is a triadic reciprocal nature to the relationship between sleep, nutrition and exercise—they are all inextricably linked to each other. There are also many factors working against human beings, particularly I would say for mums living in Western industrialised societies. Therefore, any small changes we can make to create good habits around sleep, food and exercise, have to become an important part of how we conduct ourselves in the day to day, in order to take care of these physical needs at an optimal level.

“Motherhood is the biggest gamble in the world. It is the glorious life force. It’s huge and scary—it’s an act of infinite optimism.” — Gilda Radner

# Conclusion

**Coaching**

I can't begin to round up a book about gaining the wellness needed to tap into and take note of one's knowing for mumming around without mentioning coaching. It's another invaluable tool in figuring out what our instincts are telling us about how we'd like to parent. It can help us to define our routines and stick to them. Being coached to think about and articulate our thoughts and feelings to another human being who is there completely for you, to reflect your thoughts back to you and act as your very own personal cheerleader, can be far more effective than just thinking about it on a daily basis.

**"It is what it is."**

In his final book, *Letting Go: The Pathway of Surrender*, expert psychologist Dr David R Hawkins M.D., Ph.D, presents a way of letting go of emotions that don't serve us in the moment. He suggests that emotions cause thoughts and, therefore, if we can practise noticing negative emotions and surrendering them without acting on them to try and change them, we will in turn get rid of those negative thoughts before they've had a chance to affect us. When I am operating well, this notion has changed the way I respond to most of the negative emotions I feel, and any thoughts I attempt to attach to them. I find myself often schooling my thoughts with, "it is what it is, what will be will be, let this one go, love." So much of what concerns us as mums is out of our control, and I have found an enormous amount of freedom in (a lot of the time) being able to let go of so many negative emotions that could lead to obsessive thinking about these concerns.

## What character traits do I value?

In 2004, a team of social scientists led by Christopher Peterson and Martin Seligman listed 24 character traits that make human beings the best versions of themselves. They outlined them in their book *Character Strengths and Virtues: A Handbook and Classification,* and when studying to become a mum coach, I looked into which of these I felt would be most valuable to me in my role as a mum, and to my children as I am tasked with guiding them towards becoming decent human beings. I try to live by them all, but my personal focus as a mum has been on eight of these traits: spirituality (meaning and purpose), gratitude, honesty, bravery, curiosity, kindness, positivity and fun. At the end of every day, I review how well I have practised each one in a journal. Although changes are sometimes impossible to see in real time, when I look back at my first few years mumming around and think about how markedly different my way of being is today, I can see how a large part of that has been down to bringing the awareness of these character traits to the foreground. Interestingly, the one I struggle with the most these days is "fun". I sometimes forget that it's OK to have fun. Yes, the responsibility of mumming around is big, yes, the world in which I am doing it is a crazy place and, yes, quite often, despite my best efforts, the to-do list will get the better of me, but none of that means it can't be fun. Note to self: Each moment is so fleeting and can never be a "do-over", but it can at least be fun.

**My daily routine**

I promised I would share how I incorporate the tools and guiding principles I have outlined in this book into my daily routine. I will be brief. This is shared only with the intention of imparting ideas. By no means do I think what I do is the answer. It is merely AN answer—one that works for me and the challenges in my life at this time. This routine has always been, and I'm sure will continue to be, an ever-evolving process. But for now, in order to try and live as the best version of myself whilst keeping my daily practice of the tools and guiding principles that work for me to a manageable routine, my day looks like this:

**Morning.** Wake up (I am woken up every day before six in the morning and have been every day of my mumming around life), change into workout clothes IMMEDIATELY(!) and check out an affirmation card.

Go downstairs, fill a water bottle, cut fruit for the girls and, without looking at any apps other than my Tabata timer and one needed to listen to something meaningful (a book or podcast), I do a 30 minute HIIT workout.

While I am doing that, my girls watch their tablets and snack on their fruit (and occasionally look up at me, for what I hope is some good modelling?!). I know, I know . . . they are on a screen and not eating mindfully, but I weigh it up against my wellbeing and lean into what's more important at that moment. If they ever start waking up later than six, I will perhaps have to move my exercise slot to later in the day, but at this moment in time, being forced out of bed before bird song seems like a good opportunity to engage in activity that encourages my body (and mind) into a positive state.

After a workout, I make breakfast, then plan and make everyone's lunches and snacks for the day (including mine). Then, all tech goes off, breakfast is eaten together, bodies are washed and dressed, teeth are cleaned, and we head into our day. This morning routine covers me for "be curious and learn", "exercise enough" and "eat nutritiously".

**During the day**. To the best of my ability, I eat only what I've planned, I keep tech to a minimum and try to be in nature at least once (some days, that means walking into the garden for 10 minutes with a cup of coffee and without my phone).

I try to be honest, kind, brave, positive and fun as much as possible, and when I slip (as I say, for me, this is usually with the fun part, as I get wrapped up in all the to-dos!), I try to pause and come back to these goals. If my slip has involved someone else (usually my beautiful girls—slightly sad face), I acknowledge that and rectify things with them. To make amends, I have often found that saying, "Right, please can I give you 10 minutes of mummy time? What shall we do?" fills all our cups to a level that far outweighs the sacrifice of those 10 minutes not tackling the to-do list.

An overriding tenet of my day is keeping things simple and manageable. If at any point I find there's too much in the schedule, too much expectation around things to be done, too much stuff in the house, too much sensory stimulation—just too much—I call time. And we stop and regroup. Too much is just too much!

**Evening**. I tend to clear any admin and other jobs for an hour while making dinner. The girls have their second bit of screen time, though they usually end up losing interest in what they're watching and find a game to play. During this time, I give them a big plate of veggies to snack on. Again, it goes against my ideals if they're watching a screen the whole time, but it works to get the veggies in before they come to the table for—and these are their words—"the yummy part" of dinner.

By the time we are eating together, I have very few jobs left for the day, so I can enjoy time with the girls then do bath time, book reading and sit with them while they fall asleep.

Once they are asleep, I finish anything that needs to be done and take time to myself. That could be time for checking in with a friend or watching something for enjoyment or reading a book.

**Throughout the day**. I give myself enough time before bed to meditate and write my journal. This is my chance to put down in writing how my day has gone. Was I a good person today? Did I live by my plans around learning, exercise, food, tech and being in nature? Who did I connect with? What could I have done better? Was I honest, kind, brave, positive and fun? And most importantly of all, what am I grateful for? I have found that writing gratitudes just before bed has calmed down my dreams and deepened my sleep—in as much as that's possible for any mum!

**To conclude the conclusion**

So, what have I really learned in my quest to tap into my knowing and become the best version of myself in mumming around? Well, fundamentally, I have learned about “self-care”. This is significant because these two little, innocently loving words have historically galled me to my core over the years. I would find myself tense at the proclamation of the importance of self-care by friends and health workers. It was as if, somehow, its importance had passed me by, or I was too arrogant or naive to believe its benefits would be impactful to me. Fundamentally, espousing the importance of self-care to me in previous years would have made me feel like a failure for not being able to make the time and, in some way, foolish for being unable to use what little "spare" time I had on myself, rather than my Smalls.

It’s worth acknowledging also that the advice on self-care for mums is as saturated and overwhelming as parenting advice. Start a new hobby, do some baking, go for a walk, take a long bath, have a pedicure, exercise more, volunteer, join a book club, stick affirmations on post-it notes all over your house, take a nap, get up early for an uninterrupted cup of tea, buy yourself flowers, get a massage, go out for a kid-free dinner with a partner/friend, stretch, get more sleep, listen to your favourite song, sort through your wardrobe, drink more water, have acupuncture, ask for help, plan a holiday, get reiki, do yoga, plant some flowers. The list goes on . . .

For me, however, self-care is not having a pedicure or going out with friends. It’s not taking a bath or shopping without little ones in tow—although all those things are nice. Like, *really* nice! But for me, self-care is about caring for the self. The inner self. And that doesn’t have to take all the spare hours (or should I say minutes?!) out of our day.

The self-care I practice now takes no more than an hour and a half per day in total—an hour in the morning when I’m exercising, learning and food planning, and half an hour in the evening, when I meditate and write in my journal.

During the day, my self-care takes place mainly in my head, and that's what my very simple and yet, for me, quite profound learning has been in recent years. Self-care is a way of being, not a pedicure. A way of being created by small incremental changes to life's routine. The beauty of it is that it's something entirely within our control.

What is also in my control—I'd like to add for authenticity at this point—is the amount of grace I give myself when I don't fit in the workout or am just too tired to do my journal review. Like I said, I don't have all the answers, and one of the answers I am particularly lacking is how to guarantee that nothing ever gets in the way of my plans or the way of being I would like to take into each day. But if the plan is there—if the gym clothes are ready, the book is set up to listen to and the journal is within reach, then routine becomes easier to stick to and, over time, has become something I miss enormously when out of it.

So, to my dear mumming around friends, I'd like to invite you to take control. With just a few small changes to your routine, you could very quickly find yourself working towards a greater sense of peace and happiness. Take one tool or guiding principle—or take them all. Adapt them to fit your own lifestyle and particular routine. Make today the day you commit to doing one thing that moves you closer to an improved sense of wellbeing.

Muppets creator Jim Henson said it perfectly: "The attitude you have as a parent is what your kids will learn from more than what you tell them. They don't remember what you try to teach them. They remember what you are."

I would like mine to remember me as someone who paid attention to her mental, emotional and physical wellbeing, by practising inner self-care. And, of course, who always tried to find the fun.

"I'm beginning to perceive motherhood as a long, slow letting go, of which birth is just the first step." — Sandra Steingraber

# Note from the author

If you have enjoyed this book and found it to be in service of your meaning & purpose, connection, mindfulness, learning and the overall improvement of your physical, mental and emotional wellbeing, an Amazon review from you will make it onto my gratitude list!

With love to all my fellow mums.
Please find me at www.themummingaroundcoach.com

And thank you to Anna & Darren for supporting me on this adventure.

# Chicago Tribune article

**Advice, like youth, probably just wasted on the young**

By Mary Schmich of the Chicago Tribune, 1st June 1997

Inside every adult lurks a graduation speaker dying to get out, some world-weary pundit eager to pontificate on life to young people who'd rather be Rollerblading. Most of us, alas, will never be invited to sow our words of wisdom among an audience of caps and gowns, but there's no reason we can't entertain ourselves by composing a Guide to Life for Graduates. I encourage anyone over 26 to try this and thank you for indulging my attempt.

Ladies and gentlemen of the class of '97:

Wear sunscreen.

If I could offer you only one tip for the future, sunscreen would be it. The long-term benefits of sunscreen have been proved by scientists, whereas the rest of my advice has no basis more reliable than my own meandering experience. I will dispense this advice now.

Enjoy the power and beauty of your youth. Oh, never mind. You will not understand the power and beauty of your youth until they've faded. But trust me, in 20 years, you'll look back at photos of yourself and recall in a way you can't grasp now how much possibility lay before you and how fabulous you really looked. You are not as fat as you imagine.

Don't worry about the future. Or worry, but know that worrying is as effective as trying to solve an algebra equation by chewing bubble gum. The real troubles in your life are apt to be things that never crossed your worried mind, the kind that blindside you at 4 p.m. on some idle Tuesday.

Do one thing every day that scares you.

Sing.

Don't be reckless with other people's hearts. Don't put up with people who are reckless with yours.

Floss.

Don't waste your time on jealousy. Sometimes you're ahead, sometimes you're behind. The race is long and, in the end, it's only with yourself.

Remember compliments you receive. Forget the insults. If you succeed in doing this, tell me how.

Keep your old love letters. Throw away your old bank statements.

Stretch.

Don't feel guilty if you don't know what you want to do with your life. The most interesting people I know didn't know at 22 what they wanted to do with their lives. Some of the most interesting 40-year-olds I know still don't.

Get plenty of calcium. Be kind to your knees. You'll miss them when they're gone.

Maybe you'll marry, maybe you won't. Maybe you'll have children, maybe you won't. Maybe you'll divorce at 40, maybe you'll dance the funky chicken on your 75th wedding anniversary. Whatever you do, don't congratulate yourself too much, or berate yourself either. Your choices are half chance. So are everybody else's.

Enjoy your body. Use it every way you can. Don't be afraid of it or of what other people think of it. It's the greatest instrument you'll ever own.

Dance, even if you have nowhere to do it but your living room.

Read the directions, even if you don't follow them.

Do not read beauty magazines. They will only make you feel ugly.

Get to know your parents. You never know when they'll be gone for good. Be nice to your siblings. They're your best link to your past and the people most likely to stick with you in the future.

Understand that friends come and go, but with a precious few you should hold on. Work hard to bridge the gaps in geography and lifestyle, because the older you get, the more you need the people who knew you when you were young.

Live in New York City once, but leave before it makes you hard. Live in Northern California once, but leave before it makes you soft. Travel.

Accept certain inalienable truths: Prices will rise. Politicians will philander. You, too, will get old. And when you do, you'll fantasize that when you were young, prices were reasonable, politicians were noble and children respected their elders.

Respect your elders.

Don't expect anyone else to support you. Maybe you have a trust fund. Maybe you'll have a wealthy spouse. But you never know when either one might run out.

Don't mess too much with your hair or by the time you're 40 it will look 85.

Be careful whose advice you buy, but be patient with those who supply it. Advice is a form of nostalgia. Dispensing it is a way of fishing the past from the disposal, wiping it off, painting over the ugly parts and recycling it for more than it's worth.

But trust me on the sunscreen.

# Classification of Character Strengths

**VIACHARACTER.ORG**

# Bibliography


Ockwell-Smith, S. (2021). *The Gentle Sleep Book: Gentle, No-Tears, Sleep Solutions for Parents of Newborns to Five-Year-Olds* (UK ed.). Piatkus.

Ockwell-Smith, S., & Audio Uk, H. (2022). *Beginnings: A Guide to Child Psychology and Development for Parents of 0-5-Year-Olds.* Hachette Audio UK.

Nuefeld, G., & Maté, G. *(2006) Hold On to Your Kids: Why Parents Need to Matter More Than Peers*. Ballantine Books.

Schmich, M. (2019, May 23). *Advice, like youth, probably just wasted on the young*. Chicago Tribune.

Doyle, G., & Melton, G. D. (2020). *Untamed* (Later Printing ed.). The Dial Press.

Brown, B. (2015). *Rising Strong: The Reckoning. The Rumble. The Revolution*. Random House.

Brown, B. (2019, April 19). *Brené Brown: The Call to Courage*. Netflix, Inc.

Frankl, V. E. (2004, April 30). *Man's Search for Meaning* (New Ed). Ebury Pr.

*Why it's Important to Find Your Purpose In Life (with 3 Helpful Tips)*. (2022, July 3). Tracking Happiness.

Pendell, B. R. (2022, August 11). *The World's $7.8 Trillion Workplace Problem*. Gallup.

*What Job Crafting Looks Like*. (2020, March 12). Harvard Business Review.

Santos, L. (2020, May 18). *Working your way to happiness*. Pushkin.

*Ansell: Helping others dampens the effects of everyday stress*. (2015, December 14). Yale School of Medicine.

*People who give, live longer: U-M study shows*. (2002, November 12). University of Michigan News.

*Prosociality enhances meaning in life*. (2015, June 1). Taylor & Francis.

Fone, D., White, J., Farewell, D., Kelly, M., John, G., Lloyd, K., Williams, G., & Dunstan, F. (2014). Effect of neighbourhood deprivation and social cohesion on mental health inequality: a multilevel population-based longitudinal study. *Psychological Medicine, 44*(11), 2449–2460. doi: 10.1017/S0033291713003255. Cambridge University Press.

Cherry, K. (2022, September 14). *Why Our Brains Are Hardwired to Focus on the Negative*. Verywell Mind.

*Giving thanks can make you happier*. (2021, August 14). Harvard Health Publishing.

Santos, L. (2020, March 26). *Calm Can Be Contagious*. Pushkin.

Thorpe, M., MD PhD. (2020, October 27). *12 Science-Based Benefits of Meditation*. Healthline.

Chandola, T., Booker, C. L., Kumari, M., & Benzeval, M. (2019). Are Flexible Work Arrangements Associated with Lower Levels of Chronic Stress-Related Biomarkers? A Study of 6025 Employees in the UK Household Longitudinal Study. *Sociology*, *53*(4), 779–799. doi: 10.1177/0038038519826014. SAGE JOURNALS.

Krishnamurti, J., Tedder, J., & University Press Audiobooks. (2014, March 17). *Krishnamurti: Reflections on the Self*. University Press Audiobooks.

*Six Surprising Benefits of Curiosity*. (2015, September 24). Greater Good.

von Stumm, S., Hell, B., & Chamorro-Premuzic, T. (2011, October 14). The Hungry Mind. *Perspectives on Psychological Science*, *6*(6), 574–588. doi: 10.1177/1745691611421204. SAGE JOURNALS.

*Oxford Languages | the Home of Language Data*. (2022, August 26).

Weir, K. (2020, April 1). *Nurtured by nature.* American Psychological Association.

Van Hedger, S. C., Nusbaum, H. C., Clohisy, L., Jaeggi, S. M., Buschkuehl, M., & Berman, M. G. (2018, October 26). Of cricket chirps and car horns: The effect of nature sounds on cognitive performance. *Psychonomic Bulletin &Amp; Review, 26*(2), 522–530. doi: 10.3758/s13423-018-1539-1. National Library of Medicine.

Engemann, K., Bøcker Pedersen, C., Arge, L., Svenning, J-C. (2019, February 25). Residential green space in childhood is associated with lower risk of psychiatric disorders from adolescence into adulthood. *doi: 10.1073/pnas.1807504116. PNAS*

*Children: getting them interested in gardening / RHS Gardening.* (n.d.). Royal Horticultural Society.

*About us / RHS Campaign for School Gardening.* (n.d.). Royal Horticultural Society.

Odell, J. (2020b, December 29). *How to Do Nothing: Resisting the Attention Economy.* Melville House.

Hunt, E. (2020, September 9). *Jenny Odell on why we need to learn to do nothing: 'It's a reminder that you're alive.'* The Guardian.

Favreau, J., Lovett, J., Pfeiffer, D., & Vietor, T. (2022, January 23). *Jenny Odell on How to Do Nothing.* Crooked Media.

Melore, C. (2021, October 14). *There are nearly 50 harmful effects linked to social media use.* Study Finds.

Santos, L. (2020c, June 1). *Dial D for Distracted*. Pushkin.

*Selective Attention Test.* (2010, March 10). [Video]. YouTube.

*Why Too Much Cell Phone Usage Can Hurt Your Family Relationships.* (2021, February 26). Verywell Family.

*The paradox of choice.* (2006, September 26). [Video]. TED Talks.

Schwartz, B. (2009). *The Paradox of Choice: Why More Is Less, Revised Edition*. HarperCollins.

Reutskaja E, Lindner A, Nagel R, Andersen RA, Camerer CF. Choice overload reduces neural signatures of choice set value in dorsal striatum and anterior cingulate cortex. *Nat Hum Behav*. 2018 Dec;2(12):925-935. doi: 10.1038/s41562-018-0440-2. National Library of Medicine

*Start Here to Simplify Your Life.* (2022, July 28). Be More With Less.

Carver, C. (2017). *Soulful Simplicity: How Living with Less Can Lead to So Much More*. TarcherPerigee.

Carver, C. (2020). *Project 333: The Minimalist Fashion Challenge That Proves Less Really is So Much More* (Illustrated). TarcherPerigee.

Suni, E. (2022, October 19). *How Sleep Works: Understanding the Science of Sleep*. Sleep Foundation.

*Living with Children May Mean Less Sleep for Women, But Not for Men*. (n.d.). American Academy of Neurology.

Florendo, J. (2022e, September 29). *Healthy Sleep Habits: The Ultimate Sleep Improvement Plan*. Sleep Foundation.

Fiolet, T., Srour, B., Sellem, L., Kesse-Guyot, E., Allès, B., Méjean, C., Deschasaux, M., Fassier, P., Latino-Martel, P., Beslay, M., Hercberg, S., Lavalette, C., Monteiro, C. A., Julia, C., & Touvier, M. (2018). Consumption of ultra-processed foods and cancer risk: results from NutriNet-Santé prospective cohort. *BMJ* 2018;360:k322. The BMJ.

Buettner, D. (2012). *The Blue Zones, Second Edition: 9 Lessons for Living Longer From the People Who've Lived the Longest* (2nd ed.). National Geographic.

*Physical activity*. (2022, October 5). World Health Organization.

Kyu, H. H., Bachman, V. F., Alexander, L. T., Mumford, J. E., Afshin, A., Estep, K., Veerman, J. L., Delwiche, K., Iannarone, M. L., Moyer, M. L., Cercy, K., Vos, T., Murray, C. J. L., & Forouzanfar, M. H. (2016). Physical activity and risk of breast cancer, colon cancer, diabetes, ischemic heart disease, and ischemic stroke events: systematic review and dose-response meta-analysis for the Global Burden of Disease Study 2013. *BMJ* 2016;354:i3857. The BMJ.

Hawkins, D. R, M.D. Ph.D. (2014). *Letting Go: The Pathway of Surrender* (First Edition). Hay House Inc.

Peterson, C., & Seligman, M. (2004). *Character Strengths and Virtues: A Handbook and Classification* (1st ed.). American Psychological Association / Oxford University Press.

*VIAcharacter*. (2022). VIA Institute on Character.

Printed in Great Britain
by Amazon